Scott Foresman - Addison Wesley

MATH

Problem-Solving Masters

For Guided Problem Solving

Grade 6

Scott Foresman - Addison Wesley

Editorial Offices: Glenview, Illinois • New York, New York
Sales Offices: Reading, Massachusetts • Atlanta, Georgia • Glenview, Illinois
Carrollton, Texas • Menlo Park, California

http://www.sf.aw.com

ISBN 0-201-49769-7

Printed in the United States of America

1 2 3 4 5 6 7 8 9 10 – BW – 02 01 00 99 98

Contents

Chapter 10: Ratio, Proportion, and Percent

Chapter 11: Solids and Measurement

Chapter 12: Probability

Overview

Problem-Solving Masters (For Guided Problem Solving) provide a step-by-step approach to solve a problem selected from the student book. These selections are made from the *Practice and Apply* section or from the *Problem Solving and Reasoning* section. Some of these selections are routine in nature and cover basic concepts. Others are nonroutine and might involve multiple-step problems, problems with too much information, problems involving critical thinking, and so on. An icon in the Teacher's Edition flags the selected problem so that the teacher will know what problem is provided on the master.

How to use

The Problem-Solving Masters are designed so that the teacher can use them in many different ways:

a. As a teaching tool to guide students in exploring and mastering a specific problem-solving skill or strategy. Making a transparency of the worksheet provides an excellent way to expedite this process as students work along with the teacher at their desks.

b. As additional practice in solving problems for students who have had difficulty in completing the assignment.

c. As independent or group work to help students reach a better understanding of the problem-solving process.

d. As a homework assignment that may encourage students to involve their parents in the educational process.

Description of the master

The problem to be solved is stated at the top of each master. The master is then divided into the four steps of the Problem-Solving Guidelines that are used throughout the student text. Each step includes key questions designed to guide students through the problem-solving process. At the bottom of the master, *Solve Another Problem* allows students to use their skills to solve a problem similar to the original problem. This helps reinforce the problem-solving skills and strategies they have just used in solving the problem on the master.

The Guided Problem Solving master on the next page can be used to help students organize their work as they complete the *Solve Another Problem.* It may also be used to assist students in solving any problem as they complete the four steps of the Problem-Solving Guidelines.

1. **Understand** ensures that students are able to interpret the problem and determine key facts.

2. **Plan** actively involves students in devising a plan or strategy for solving the problem. They may be asked to choose a fact or formula that could be used to solve the problem. In other cases, students may be asked to model the problem or draw a picture. Other times, students will be asked to choose a strategy they can use to solve the problem. Problem-solving strategies often used include: Look for a Pattern, Make a Table, Work Backward, Draw a Diagram, Make an Organized List, Guess and Check, Use Logical Reasoning, and Solve a Simpler Problem.

3. **Solve** encourages students to carry out the plan and arrive at an answer. Students may be asked to answer the question using a full sentence.

4. **Look Back** encourages students to review their work and check their answer to see if it is reasonable. This step often asks students to reflect on the strategy they used or to suggest other strategies they could also have used to solve the problem. It is important that students think of this step as a natural part of the problem-solving process.

Name ______________________________

Guided Problem Solving

Understand

Plan

Solve

Look Back

Name ________________________________

Guided Problem Solving
1-1

Ocean sizes are often measured in square miles. Use this measurement and the graph to answer the question.

The total area of the Pacific, Atlantic, and Indian Oceans is 124,000,000 square miles. How many square miles is the Pacific Ocean?

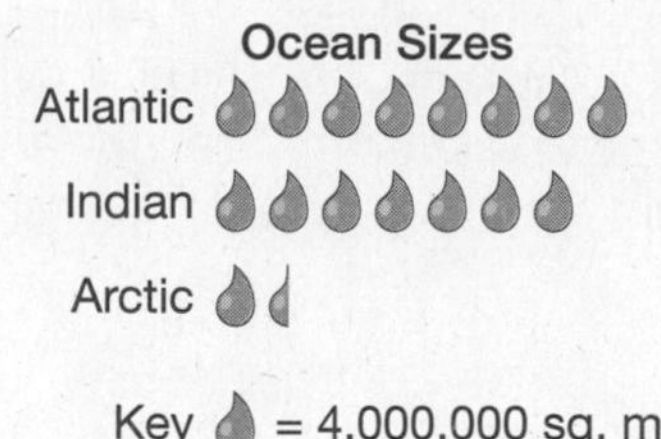

Understand

1. What does the problem ask you to find?

____

2. Which oceans have a combined area of 124,000,000 square miles?

____

Plan

3. Use the graph. What is the area of

a. the Atlantic Ocean? ____________ **b.** the Indian Ocean? ____________

4. What is the combined area of the Atlantic and Indian Oceans? ____________

Solve

5. Write a number sentence to find the area of the Pacific Ocean.

____

6. What is the area of the Pacific Ocean? ____________

Look Back

7. How can you use addition to check your answer?

____

____

SOLVE ANOTHER PROBLEM

The total area of the Arctic and Indian Oceans, and the South China Sea is 35,000,000 square miles.

How many square miles is the South China Sea? ____________

Name ______________________________

Guided Problem Solving
1-2

Use the population graph.
How many more 5–13 year-olds will there be in the year 2000 than there were in the year when their population was the smallest?

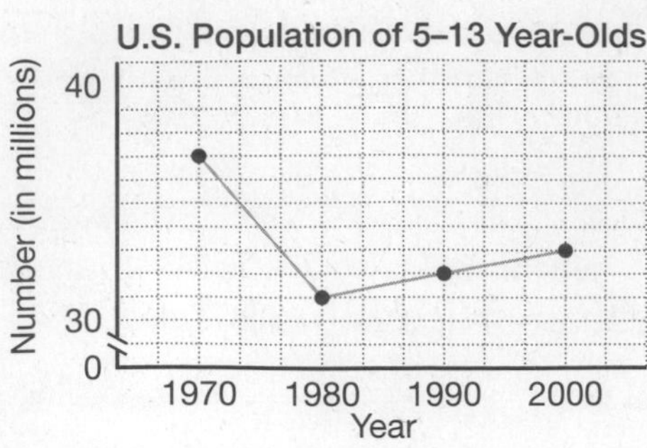

Understand

1. Circle the question.
2. How do you find the number of 5–13 year-olds for 1970?

____

____

3. What does the jagged line represent on the vertical scale?

____

Plan

4. What year was the population of 5–13 year-olds the smallest? ________
5. How many 5–13 year-olds were there in the year the population was the smallest? ____________
6. How many 5–13 year-olds will there be in the year 2000? ____________

Solve

7. Choose the number sentence you will use to solve the problem. ________

a. 33 + 31 = 64 **b.** 33 − 31 = 2 **c.** 37 − 31 = 6

8. Write your answer in a complete sentence.

____

Look Back

9. How could you have solved the problem in another way?

____

____

SOLVE ANOTHER PROBLEM

How many more 5–13 year-olds were there in the year 1990 than in the year 1980? ____________

Name ______________________________

Guided Problem Solving
1-3

Use the Calorie Requirements graph. At what age is the difference in calorie needs the greatest between males and females? The smallest? How can you tell?

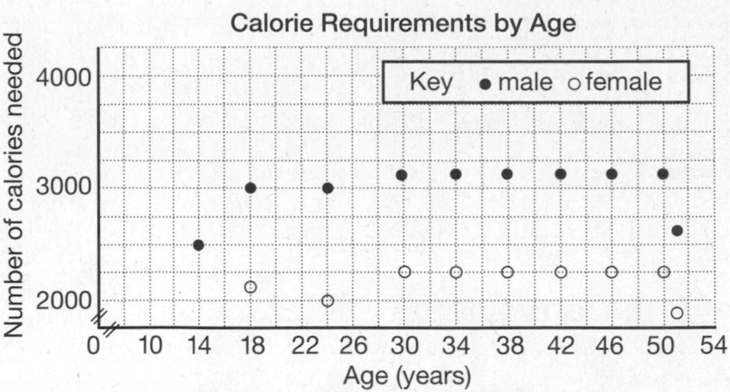

Understand

1. What do these points represent?

   a. solid ______________________

   b. open ______________________

2. What does the distance between two points at any age represent?

____

Plan

3. The greatest distance between two points for any age is at age ________.

4. The smallest distance between two points for any age is at age ________.

Solve

5. At what age is the difference in calorie needs the greatest between males and females? How can you tell? ______________________

____

6. At what age is the difference in calorie needs the smallest between males and females? How can you tell? ______________________

____

Look Back

7. How can you use subtraction to verify your answer? ______________________

____

____

SOLVE ANOTHER PROBLEM

At what ages is the difference in calorie needs about the same? ______________

Name ____________________

Guided Problem Solving
1-4

Draw a line plot of the ages of the first ten Presidents when they took office.

Age of First Ten Presidents

Age	Frequency
51	1
54	1
57	4
58	1
61	2
68	1

Understand

1. What are you asked to do?

____

____

2. What mark do you use to record an item of data on a line plot? ________

Plan

3. List the Presidents' ages. ____________________

4. The smallest number you record is ________.

5. The largest number you record is ________.

6. How many marks will you write for one President's age? ____________

Solve

7. Write the ages in order from youngest to oldest on the line plot. Include all ages between the youngest and oldest.

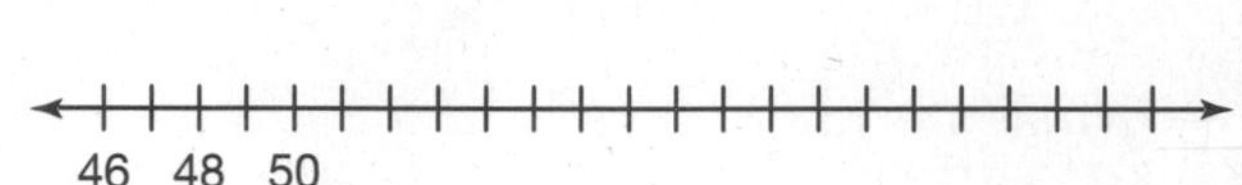

8. Record the data.

Look Back

9. How can you make sure that you have recorded each data item in the line plot? ____________________

____

SOLVE ANOTHER PROBLEM

Make a line plot to represent the value of the coins in this data set: dime, nickel, dime, penny, nickel, penny, dime, dime, penny, nickel, nickel, penny, penny, dime, dime, nickel, penny, nickel, dime, dime

Name ______________________________

Guided Problem Solving 1-5

Many people consider Presidential burial grounds to be of important historical value. The first 20 Presidents were buried in the following states: Illinois (1), Kentucky (1), Massachusetts (2), New Hampshire (1), New York (3), Ohio (3), Pennsylvania (1), Tennessee (3), Vermont (5).

a. What is the range of values in this set of data?

b. Make a bar graph of the data.

Understand

1. How can you find the range?

____

Plan

2. What will each axis on your graph will represent? ______________________________

____

3. What interval will you use on the axis showing the number of Presidents buried in each state? Explain. ______________________________

____

Solve

4. What is the range of values? ________

5. Draw and shade the bars that represent the number of burial grounds for each state. The one for Illinois is completed for you. Give the graph a title.

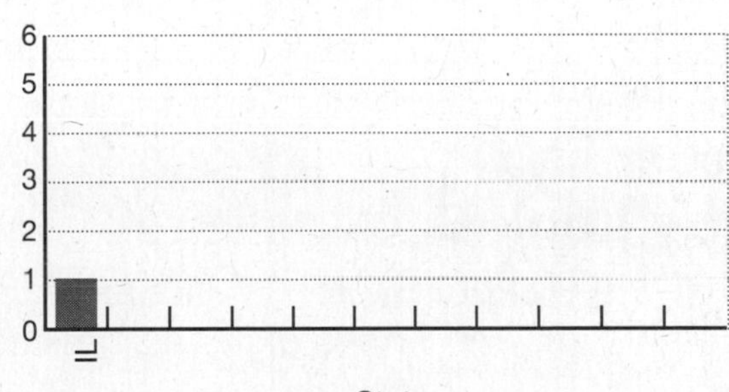

Look Back

6. How can you make sure you have graphed the data accurately?

____

____

SOLVE ANOTHER PROBLEM

The next three Presidents were buried in New York, New Jersey, and Indiana. Use a different color pencil to add this information to your graph. How does this affect the range?

____

Name ______________________________

Guided Problem Solving
1-6

Make a stem-and-leaf diagram from the data.

The ten fastest fish in the world (in miles per hour) include the following: sailfish, 68; blue shark, 43; swordfish, 40; marlin, 50; bluefin tuna, 46; wahoo, 41; tarpon, 35; bonefish, 40; yellowfin tuna, 44; tiger shark, 33.

Understand

1. Underline the speed of each fish.
2. What are you asked to make from the data? ________

   a. bar graph **b.** scatterplot **c.** stem-and-leaf diagram

Plan

3. Write the stems from least to greatest. Then write each leaf to the right of its stem as it occurs in the problem.

Stem	Leaf

Solve

4. Redraw the stem-and-leaf diagram, with the leaves in order from least to greatest.

Stem	Leaf

Look Back

5. Did you put the tens digits as "stems" and ones digits as "leaves"? ______________________
6. What other ways could you display the data? ______________________

SOLVE ANOTHER PROBLEM

Make a stem-and-leaf diagram to organize these data. The average lengths (in feet) of some of the fastest fish in the world are: sailfish, 8; swordfish, 11; marlin, 35; bluefin tuna, 14; wahoo, 3; tarpon, 8; bonefish, 2; yellowfin tuna, 11. Hint: Use zero as one of the stems.

Stem	Leaf

Stem	Leaf

Name ______________________________

Guided Problem Solving
1-7

Find the median and mode number of counties for the 11 western states shown in the map.

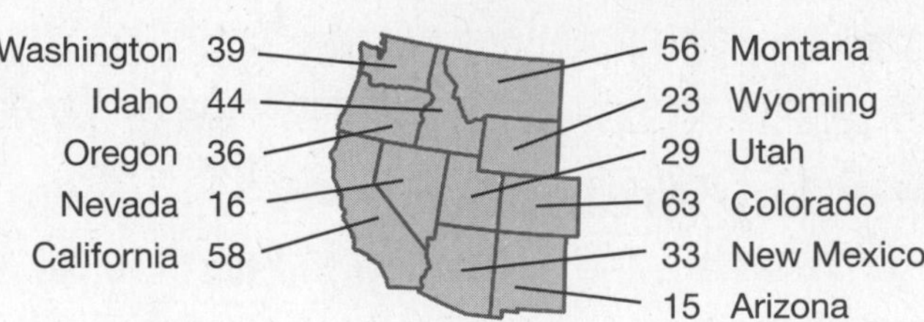

Understand

1. What are you asked to find? ______________________________

Plan

2. Explain what you need to do to find the median or the mode.

Solve

3. Write the numbers in order from least to greatest.

4. Write the median. ______________

5. Write the mode. ______________

Look Back

6. What are some different ways you can organize the information given in the problem?

SOLVE ANOTHER PROBLEM

Find the median and mode number of counties or parishes for these 16 southern states: Alabama, 67; Arkansas, 75; Delaware, 3; Florida, 67; Georgia, 159; Kentucky, 120; Louisiana, 64; Maryland, 23; Mississippi, 82; North Carolina, 100; Oklahoma, 77, South Carolina, 46, Tennessee, 95, Texas, 254, Virginia, 95, and West Virginia, 55.

Name ______________________________

Guided Problem Solving
1-8

Suppose you have test scores of 92, 85, 86, and 90. What would you need to score on the next test to have a mean score of 90?

Understand

1. What are the scores on the first four tests? ______________

2. What is the mean score you want after five tests? ______

3. How do you find the mean of a set of data? ______________________________

____

____

Plan

4. Which operation will you use to find the total score of four tests. ______________

5. Which operation will you use to find the total score you should have on five tests if the mean score is 90? ______________

6. Which operation will you use to find the score you need on the fifth test? ______________

Solve

7. What is the total of the first four test scores? ______

8. What is the total you would need on five tests to have a mean score of 90 points? ______

9. What do you need to score on the fifth test? ______

Look Back

10. How can you check to see if your answer is reasonable? ______________

____

____

SOLVE ANOTHER PROBLEM

Suppose you are on a trip. You have traveled 50 miles, 60 miles, 140 miles, 200 miles, and 10 miles. How far must you travel tomorrow to have a mean distance of 100 miles? ______________

Name ______________________________

Guided Problem Solving
1-9

a. Find the mean, median, and mode with and without the outlier.

b. Did the outlier affect the mode? The mean? The median? Which did it affect the most?

Dinah Shore Tournament Scores (1996)	
Nanci Bowen	285
Susie Redman	286
Brandie Burton	287
Sherri Turner	287
Meg Mallon	292

Understand

1. How many times will you need to find the mean, median, and mode for this set of data? ______________

Plan

2. Write the data in order from least to greatest. Underline the outlier. ______________

Solve

3. Complete the table to find the means, medians, and modes.

	With outlier	Without outlier
Mean		
Median		
Mode		

4. How did the outlier affect the mean, median, and mode?

____

____

5. Which did the outlier affect the most? ______________

Look Back

6. How can you tell if your answer to Item 4 is reasonable? ______________

____

____

SOLVE ANOTHER PROBLEM

For these scores, calculate the mean, median, and mode, with and without the outlier: 35, 82, 85, 85, 90, 93.

____

____

Name ______________________________

Guided Problem Solving
2-1

For the fact, write the number in word form and in number-word form.

Neptune's mean distance from the sun is 2,798,800,000 miles.

Understand

1. How many digits are there in the number? ____________

2. In which forms will you write the number? ____________

Plan

3. Write each number of trillions, billions, millions, thousands, and ones.

   a. Trillions ______ b. Billions ______ c. Millions ______

   d. Thousands ______ e. Ones ______

4. Which places have zeros? What is the greatest place value you will use when you write the number in number-word form?

   ____

Solve

5. Write the number in number-word form.

   ____

6. Write the entire number in words. ______________________________

   ____

   ____

Look Back

7. How can you check your work by reading each number aloud?

   ____

   ____

SOLVE ANOTHER PROBLEM

For the fact, write the number in word form and in number-word form.

Light travels 5,880,000,000,000 miles in one year.

____

Name ______________________________

Guided Problem Solving
2-2

On August 29, 1989, the planetary explorer *Voyager 2* crossed Pluto's orbit and left the solar system. *Voyager 2* was 2,758,530,928 miles from Earth. Round *Voyager 2*'s distance to the given place.

a. hundred-thousands
b. ten-millions
c. hundred-millions
d. billions

Understand

1. How many different place-values are you asked round to? ________

2. If the digit to the right of the place-value you are rounding to is less than 5, will the place-value digit increase by 1 or remain the same? ____________

Plan

3. What is the place-value digit and the digit to the right of each place-value?

a. hundred-thousands ________
b. ten-millions ________
c. hundred-millions ________
d. billions ________

Solve

4. Round the distance to the given place value. Remember to write the digits to the right of the place-value digit as zeros.

a. hundred-thousands ________________
b. ten-millions ________________
c. hundred-millions ________________
d. billions ________________

Look Back

5. If you rounded all your answers in Question 4 to the nearest billion, would they all be the same? Explain.

____

____

____

SOLVE ANOTHER PROBLEM

Round 6,832,149,520 to the given place.

a. ten-thousands ________________
b. millions ________________
c. hundred-millions ________________
d. billions ________________

Name ______________________________

Guided Problem Solving 2-3

The bar graph shows the five most populated metropolitan areas in the United States, according to the 1990 census.

The populations of the five areas are 18,087,251; 6,253,311; 14,531,529; 8,065,633; and 5,899,345. Match each area with its population.

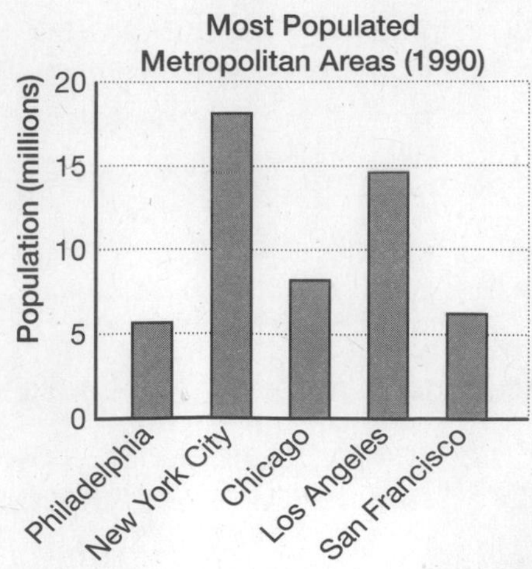

Understand

1. Underline what you are asked to do.
2. Circle the information you need.

Plan

3. Does Los Angeles or Chicago have the greater population. Explain. ______________________________

Solve

4. Use the bar graph. Order the areas from least to greatest population.

   ________ ________ ________ ________ ________

5. Order the populations given from least to greatest.

   ________ ________ ________ ________ ________

6. Match each area with its population.

   ____

   ____

Look Back

7. How could you solve the problem another way? ______________________________

   ____

SOLVE ANOTHER PROBLEM

When graphed, the height of the bar showing the population of Istanbul falls between the bars of Chicago and San Francisco. Which of the following is an approximation of its population? ________

a. 8,865,000 **b.** 5,890,000 **c.** 6,461,000

Name ______________________________

Guided Problem Solving
2-4

Find each number.

a. Find the number that equals 100 when it is squared.

b. Find the number that equals 27 when it is cubed.

Understand

1. Circle the information you need.

2. What does "squared" mean? ______________________________

3. What does "cubed" mean? ______________________________

Plan

4. How can finding the factors of each number help you solve the problem? ______________________________

____

5. What are the factors of 100? ______________________________

6. What are the factors of 27? ______________________________

Solve

7. Multiply each factor by itself the appropriate number of times. Which factor in Item 5 will equal 100 when squared? ________

8. Multiply each factor by itself the appropriate number of times. Which factor in Item 6 will equal 27 when cubed? ________

Look Back

9. Write a number sentence using exponents to show each answer.

____

10. How could you have found the answer using a different strategy?

____

SOLVE ANOTHER PROBLEM

Find each number.

a. Find the number which equals 225 when it is squared. ________

b. Find the number which equals 512 when it is cubed. ________

Name ______________________________

Guided Problem Solving
2-5

At the Metropolitan Coin Fair, Robbie sold 99 coins from his collection of 876. How many coins did he have left?

Understand

1. What are you asked to find? ______________________________

Plan

2. What operation will you use to find the answer? ____________

3. Which method could be used to solve the problem using mental math? ______

   a. compensation b. compatible numbers c. Distributive Property

4. Why did you choose that method? ______________________________

____

____

5. Which of the following is a good estimate of the answer? ______

   a. about 900 b. about 800 c. about 700

Solve

6. Write a number sentence to show the total number of coins in Robbie's collection. ______________________________

7. How many coins did Robbie have left? __________

Look Back

8. How else could you have used compensation to find the answer?

____

____

9. How can you check your answer?

____

____

SOLVE ANOTHER PROBLEM

Joanna has a collection of 145 toys from fast-food children's meals. She gave 27 toys to her sister. How many does she have now? __________

Name ______________________________

Guided Problem Solving
2-6

A picture frame measures 36 in. by 18 in. Estimate the distance around the outside of the frame.

Understand

1. Underline what you are asked to do.
2. What are the dimensions of the frame? ____________

Plan

3. Draw a picture of the rectangular frame. Label the length of each side.
4. Which numbers will you add to find the total distance around the frame? ____________
5. Will you use front end-estimation or clustering to estimate the answer. Why? ____________

____

Solve

6. Write a number sentence showing the numbers you used to estimate your answer.

____

7. Write a sentence to give the estimated distance around the frame.

____

____

Look Back

8. How could you find your answer in another way?

____

SOLVE ANOTHER PROBLEM

A rectangular dog pen measures 96 in. by 84 in. Estimate the distance around the outside of the dog pen. Show the numbers you used to estimate.

____

Name ______________________________

Guided Problem Solving
2-7

Flight 777 carries 54 passengers, each with 2 suitcases. Each suitcase weighs, on average, 36 pounds. If the airplane was built to carry 5000 pounds of luggage, is the flight over or under its limit?

Understand

1. What are you asked to find? ______________________________

____

Plan

2. Why is it acceptable to estimate to find the answer? ______________________________

____

3. Which method will you use to estimate? ________

   a. Front-end estimation   b. Rounding   c. Compensation

Solve

4. Estimate the number of suitcases that are on the plane.

   ________ × ________ = ________

5. Estimate the total number of pounds that the suitcases weigh.

   ________ × ________ = ________

6. Compare your estimate to 5000 lb.
   Is the flight over or under its limit? __________

Look Back

7. How could you have solved the problem another way?

____

____

____

SOLVE ANOTHER PROBLEM

Flight 897 carries 48 passengers, each with 2 suitcases. Each suitcase weighs, on average, 43 pounds. If the airplane was built to carry 4800 pounds of luggage, is the flight over or under its limit?

____

Name ______________________________

Guided Problem Solving
2-8

Find an arithmetic expression equal to 9 that contains the following operations.

a. Addition and division
b. Subtraction and division
c. Addition, multiplication, and an exponent

Understand

1. What number must each expression equal? ________

2. How many expressions will you write? ______________

Plan

3. How many operations will you perform in each expression?

a. Part a ________ **b.** Part b ________ **c.** Part c ________

4. Which operation will you perform first in each expression?

a. Part a ____________ **b.** Part b ____________ **c.** Part c ____________

Solve

5. To write expression a, choose two numbers and perform the first operation. Show the numbers you choose. ____________

6. What number would you need to use with the second operation so that the value of the expression is 9? Write the expression. If you cannot find a number, change the numbers you used in Item 5. ____________

7. Repeat the steps in Items 5 and 6 to write expression b. ____________

8. To write expression c, repeat the step in Item 5. Choose a number and perform the second operation. Then repeat the steps in Item 7. ____________

Look Back

9. Find another solution for each problem.

____

SOLVE ANOTHER PROBLEM

Write an arithmetic expression equal to 12 which contains subtraction, an exponent, and division.

____

Name ______________________________

Guided Problem Solving
2-9

Jeff is conducting a science experiment with a three-rabbit population. Every month, the rabbit population doubles. How many rabbits will he have after 5 months?

Understand

1. Circle the information you need.
2. What does it mean for the population to "double?" ______________________
3. Will the rabbit population get larger or smaller? ____________

Plan

4. Will you use addition or multiplication to solve the problem? ____________
5. What is the numerical pattern? ______________________________
6. Which would be a reasonable answer for the number of rabbits Jeff will have in 5 months? ______

   a. about 20   **b.** about 200   **c.** about 2000

Solve

7. How many rabbits will Jeff have after 1 month? __________
8. Continue the pattern for months 1, 2, 3, 4, and 5.

   3, ______, ______, ______, ______, ______
   after: 1 mo 2 mo 3 mo 4 mo 5 mo

9. Write a sentence to give the final answer. ______

   ____

   ____

Look Back

10. What other strategies could you have used to find the answer?

    ____

    ____

SOLVE ANOTHER PROBLEM

Marie is conducting a science experiment with a four-mouse population. Every 2 months, the mouse population doubles. How many mice will she have after 8 months? __________

Name ______________________

Guided Problem Solving
2-10

Complete the table. An average blue whale eats 9000 pounds of food each day.

Amount of Food (lb)	Number of Days
63,000	
81,000	
126,000	
f	

Understand

1. How many pounds of food does an average blue whale eat each day?

____

2. What do you need to find to complete the table? ______________

____

3. What does *f* represent in the table? ______________

Plan

4. What operation will you use to complete the table? ______________

5. How can you use patterns to find your answer? ______________

____

Solve

6. Write the expression you used to find the number of days it takes to eat 63,000 lb of food. ______________

7. Write the expression you would use to find the number of days it would take to eat *f* pounds of food. ______________

8. Complete the table above.

Look Back

9. How can you be sure that the expression you wrote for *f* days is correct?

____

SOLVE ANOTHER PROBLEM

Complete the table. A wild elephant eats 500 pounds of food each day.

Amount of Food (lb)	Number of Days
4,000	
10,500	
x	

Name ______________________________

Guided Problem Solving
2-11

Write an expression for the distance around each square.

a. 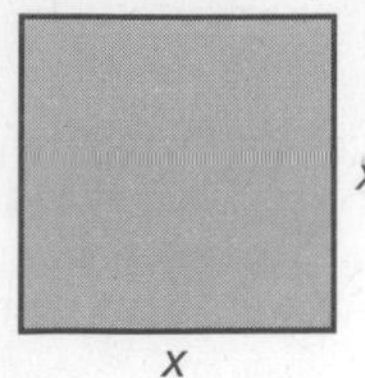

b. 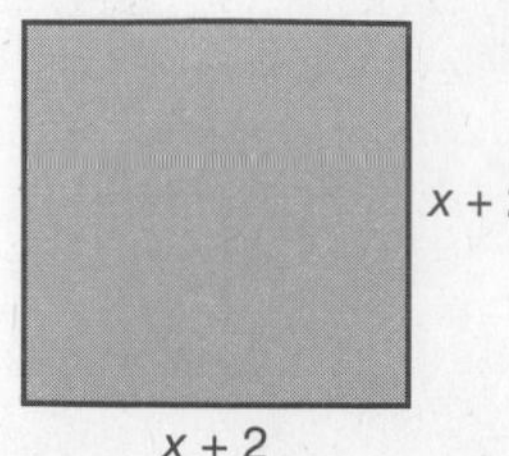

c. 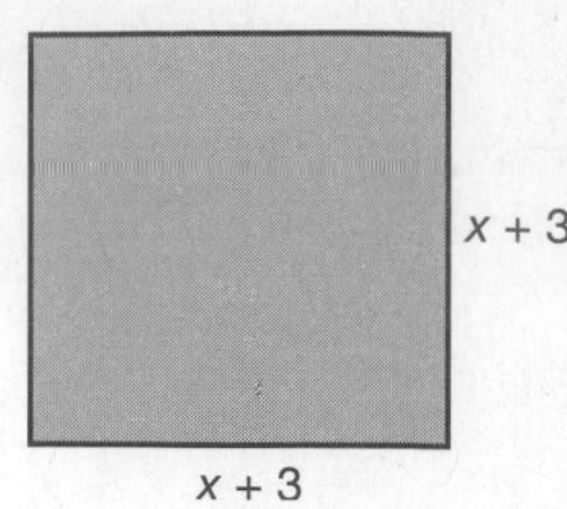

Understand

1. What is the length of each side of the square shown in

a. square **a**? ________ **b.** square **b**? ________ **c.** square **c**? ________

2. How do you find the distance around a square? ______________________

3. How many expressions will you write? ______________

Plan

4. Write an expression showing the distance around a square when each side of the square is 10 cm? ______________________

Solve

5. Write an expression for distance around square a by substituting the length of the side for 10 in the expression you wrote in Item 4. ________

6. Repeat the steps in Item 5 to write an expression for the distance around square b. ______________________

7. Repeat the steps in Item 5 to write an expression for the distance around square c. ______________________

Look Back

8. You solved a simpler problem to find the answer. What other strategy could you have used? ______________________

SOLVE ANOTHER PROBLEM

Write an expression for the distance around each equilateral triangle?

a. 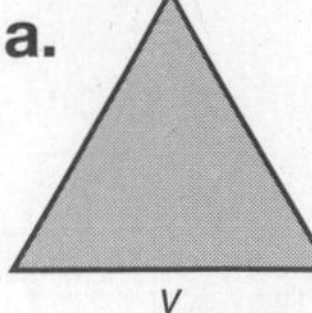

b. 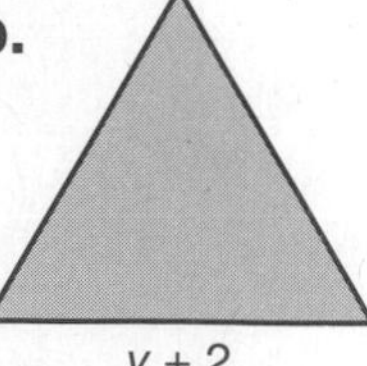

c. 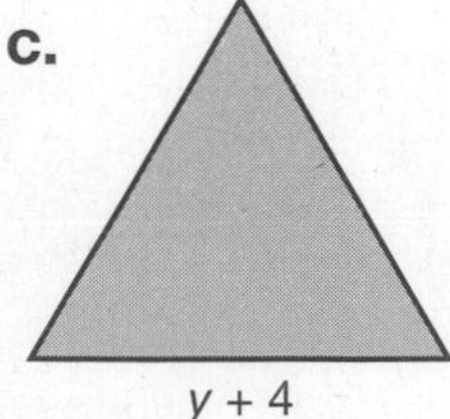

________ ________ ________

Name ______________________________

Guided Problem Solving
2-12

Franz and Jenna built a rectangular treehouse. The north and south walls were each f feet long. The east and west walls were $f + 2$ feet long. The total distance around the treehouse was 24 feet. Was the north wall 6 feet long? Explain.

Understand

1. How do you find the distance around a rectangular figure?

____

2. What is the distance around the treehouse? __________

3. What are the dimensions of the treehouse? __________

Plan

4. Write an equation showing the distance around the treehouse.

____

Solve

5. Substitute 6 for f in your equation. If the north wall is 6 feet long, what is the distance around the treehouse? __________

6. Could the treehouse have a north wall that is 6 feet long? Explain.

____

____

Look Back

7. What is another strategy you could use to solve the problem?

____

SOLVE ANOTHER PROBLEM

The Hot Shot Club placed a colored border around the outside of the hallway bulletin board. They used 32 feet of crepe paper. The width of the bulletin board was w feet. The length was $w + 4$ feet. Was the width of the bulletin board 6 feet long? Explain.

____

____

Name ______________________________

Guided Problem Solving
2-13

Write an equation for the situation and then solve it.

The top three gold-producing countries produce 1171 tonnes (metric tons) of gold. South Africa produces 584 tonnes. Australia produces 256 tonnes. The United States produces *u* tonnes. How much does the United States produce?

Understand

1. Circle the number of tonnes produced by each country.
2. How many tonnes are produced by the three countries? ______________

Plan

3. What operation would you use to find the total number of tonnes produced by the three countries? ______________
4. Write an expression showing the number of tonnes produced by the three countries. ______________

Solve

5. Write an equation showing the gold production for the three countries. Use your answer to Item 4 as one side of the equation.

____

6. How much gold did South Africa and Australia produce in all? ______________
7. Substitute the total tonnes produced by South Africa and Australia for the two values in your equation. Rewrite the equation.

____

8. Solve the equation. How much does the United States produce? ______________

Look Back

9. How can you check you answer to be sure it is correct?

____

____

SOLVE ANOTHER PROBLEM

Write and solve an equation: One year, Ghana produced 26 tonnes of gold, Mexico produced 9 tonnes, and China produced *g* tonnes. Together they produced 155 tonnes. How much did China produce?

____

Name ______________________________

Guided Problem Solving 3-1

Jarvis made a four-digit number with 0, 3, 6, and 8. The number was smaller than 5 but bigger than 1. What could his number be? Explain.

Understand

1. How many digits will there be in Jarvis's number? __________

2. Underline the clue that helps you find the first digit.

Plan

3. Is Jarvis's number a whole number or a decimal? Explain.

____

____

Solve

4. Write the first digit of one number made from 0, 3, 6, and 8 in the first box at the right. Explain how you know.

____

5. Write the remaining digits in as many ways as you can.

____

6. Look at each way you listed the digits in Item 5. Does the order of the remaining three digits make any difference in whether the number is less than 5 or greater than 1? Explain.

____

Look Back

7. What strategy can you use to make sure that you have listed all the possible numbers that meet the criteria?

____

SOLVE ANOTHER PROBLEM

Agatha made a five-digit number with 0, 3, 5, 8, and 9. The number is bigger than 39 and smaller than 53. The thousandths digit is 3 times the tenths digit. What number did Agatha make? __________

Name ______________________________

Guided Problem Solving
3-2

Wendell and Terry both rounded the number 3.4682. Wendell says that he rounded the number up. Terry says that he rounded the number down. To what place value might the number have been rounded by Wendell? By Terry? Explain.

Understand

1. Underline the information that you need.

Plan

2. When is a number rounded up? ______________________________

____

Solve

3. Would you round each number up or down when rounding to the

   a. ones place? __________ b. tenths place? __________

   c. hundredths place? __________ d. thousandths place? __________

4. Wendell rounded up. List all the place values that the number might have been rounded to by Wendell. Explain.

____

5. Terry rounded down. List all the place values that the number might have been rounded to by Terry. Explain.

____

Look Back

6. Why didn't you check ten-thousandths as a place value?

____

SOLVE ANOTHER PROBLEM

Casey and Jenna both rounded the number 42.185. Casey rounded the number up. Jenna rounded the number down. To what place value might the number have been rounded by Casey? By Jenna? Explain.

____

____

____

Name ______________________________

Guided Problem Solving
3-3

The chart shows the finishing times for a swimming race. Who came in first, second, and third?

Swimmer	Time (sec)
Gabe	32.01
Raul	31.84
Josh	31.92

Understand

1. How long did it take Raul to finish the race? ____________

2. Is the fastest time less than or greater than the slowest time? Explain.

____

____

Plan

3. To list the times in order, which digits will you compare first? ____________

Second? ____________ Third? ____________ Fourth? ____________

Solve

4. Write the times in order from least to greatest. ____________

5. Write the times in order from fastest to slowest. ____________

6. Who came in first? ____________ Second? ____________ Third? ____________

Look Back

7. Did you need to compare all the place values to order the times? Explain.

____

____

SOLVE ANOTHER PROBLEM

The chart shows the finishing times for a relay race. Who came in first, second, and third?

____

Runner	Time (sec)
Lynn	28.10
Kenisha	28.01
Raylene	21.08

Name ______________________________

Guided Problem Solving
3-4

In 1993, the U.S. Post Office released a large number of stamps picturing Elvis Presley. In scientific notation, the exponent is 8. The decimal factor has three digits, all of them odd. It's greater than 5.13, less than 5.19, and all the digits are different. How many Elvis Presley stamps were issued in 1993?

Understand

1. What are you asked to find? ______________________________

____

2. How will the number of stamps be written? ________

a. Standard notation **b.** Scientific notation

Plan

3. Write the power of ten for the number of stamps. ________

4. The digits in the decimal factor are odd.
Which digits could be in the decimal factor? ____________

5. The decimal factor is between 5.13 and 5.19. Which digit is

a. in the ones place? ________ **b.** in the tenths place? ________

c. Since no digit can be repeated in the answer, which digit can be used in the hundredths place? ________

Solve

6. Combine the information you found in Items 4 and 5 to write a sentence stating how many Elvis stamps were issued in 1993.

____

____

Look Back

7. Which strategy did you use to find your answer? ______________________________

SOLVE ANOTHER PROBLEM

A number in scientific notation uses only digits that are multiples of 3, except for the base of 10 in the power of ten. Each digit is used once and the number is the largest number possible. What is the number?

____

Name ______________________________

Guided Problem Solving
3-5

You bought four pairs of pants at the same price. Based on rounding, your estimate of the total cost was $40 before tax.

a. If you rounded to the nearest dollar, what is the maximum price for each pair? Explain.

b. If you rounded to the nearest dollar, what is the minimum price? Explain.

Understand

1. Underline the information you need.

2. To estimate, you will round to the nearest ______________.

Plan

3. Each pair of pants costs the same amount. What is the estimated cost of each pair of pants? __________

4. To find the maximum price, will you look for a number that rounds up or rounds down to 10? Explain. ____________________

____

Solve

5. What is the maximum price for each pair of pants? __________

6. What is the minimum price for each pair of pants? __________

Look Back

7. Write number sentences to check your answers. ____________________

____

SOLVE ANOTHER PROBLEM

You bought three CDs at the same price. Based on rounding, your estimate of the total cost was $36 before tax. If you rounded to the nearest dollar, what is the maximum price for each CD? What is the minimum price? Explain your answers.

____

____

____

Name ______________________________

Guided Problem Solving
3-6

One day, 1 Japanese yen was worth 0.0098 U.S. dollars.
The same day, a Swedish krona was worth 0.1297 U.S. dollars.

a. How much more was the krona worth than the yen that day?

b. On the same day, 1 Thai baht was worth 0.0398 U.S. dollars. How much U.S. money equals one baht plus one yen?

Understand

1. How many U.S. dollars was one Japanese yen worth? __________

2. How many U.S. dollars was one Swedish krona worth? __________

3. How many U.S. dollars was one Thai baht worth? __________

Plan

4. Which operation will you use to find how much more one currency is than another? ______________

5. Which operation will you use to find how much two currencies are worth together? ______________

Solve

6. How much more was the krona worth than the yen? Compare in U.S. dollars. __________

7. How many U.S. dollars equal one baht plus one yen? __________

Look Back

8. Would a grid model help you find the answer? Explain.

____

____

SOLVE ANOTHER PROBLEM

One day, 1 Canadian dollar was worth 0.7319 U.S. dollars. The same day, a German mark was worth 0.6430 U.S. dollars.

a. How much more was the Canadian dollar worth than the German mark that day? __________

b. On the same day, 1 Pakistani rupee was worth 0.0252 U.S. dollars. How much U.S. money equals one mark plus one rupee? __________

Name ___________________________

Jorge won a cash prize in a contest. He donated half of the money to his Boy Scout troop. Then he spent $19.49 on a computer game and put the rest, $30.51 into his savings account. How much money did he win?

Understand

1. What are you asked to find? ___________________________

2. What was the first thing Jorge did with his winnings? ___________________________

____

3. What were the second and third things Jorge did with his winnings? ___________

____

____

Plan

4. Which strategy will you use to find the answer? ________

   a. Work Backward **b.** Look for a Pattern **c.** Make a Table

5. Jorge donated half of his winnings to the Boy Scouts. What fraction did he spend on other things? ___________

6. What is the first operation you will use? ___________

Solve

7. How much money did Jorge have before he bought the game? ________

8. How much did Jorge win in the contest? ________

Look Back

9. What other strategies could you use to find the answer? ___________

____

____

SOLVE ANOTHER PROBLEM

Hector received some cash for his birthday. He spent $14.30 on a CD and donated $25.00 to a charity. He put half of what was left into his savings account. He has $17.85 left. How much money did he receive on his birthday? ________

Name ______________________

Guided Problem Solving
3-8

Andrea drinks 54.3 ounces of milk every week. She also drinks a 6-ounce can of orange juice and 8 glasses of water every day. If she drinks 544.3 ounces of liquid in a week and every glass of water is the same size, how big is each glass of water?

Understand

1. What are you asked to find? ______________________
2. Circle the data given in ounces per week.
3. Underline the data given in ounces per day.

Plan

4. How will you find how much Andrea drinks in one week when you are given the amount she drinks each day? ______________
5. How many glasses of water does she drink each day? ______________
6. How many glasses of water does she drink each week? ______________
7. How many ounces of orange juice does she drink each week? ______________

Solve

8. How many ounces of milk and juice does she drink each week? ______________
9. Subtract to find how many ounces of water she drinks each week. ______________
10. Divide by 56 to find how many ounces each glass of water holds. ______________

Look Back

11. How can you work backward to check your answer? ______________

____

____

SOLVE ANOTHER PROBLEM

Kelsey earns $65.30 every week working at a grocery store and $5 every day walking a neighbor's dog. She also watches her brother for 2 hours every day. If she earns $128.30 each week, how much does she earn each hour she watches her brother? ______________

Name ______________________________

Guided Problem Solving
3-9

Estimate first. Then solve.

In 1863, emigrants could buy rice for $0.11 per pound in Chimney Rock, Nebraska. The Wilson's barrel could hold 19.25 pounds. How much did it cost to fill the barrel?

Understand

1. Circle the information you need.

Plan

2. Which operation will you use to find the cost to fill the barrel? ____________
3. Estimate your answer by rounding.

   a. Round $0.11 to the nearest tenth. ______

   b. Round $19.25 to the nearest ten. ______

Solve

4. Use your rounded numbers to estimate the cost. ______
5. Find the actual cost to fill the barrel.
   Round your answer to the nearest cent. ______

Look Back

6. How can you tell if your answer is reasonable?

   ____

   ____

7. Why did you have to round your answer to Item 5?

   ____

   ____

SOLVE ANOTHER PROBLEM

Estimate first. Then solve.

In 1996, brown rice cost $1.09 per pound. How much would it cost the Wilsons to fill their 19.25-pound barrel with rice in 1996?

____

Name ______________________

Guided Problem Solving
3-10

In a gymnastic competition, Dominique scored 9.5, 9.6, 9.5, 9.4, 9.7, and 9.6. Kim scored 9.5, 9.4, 9.6, 9.7, 9.7, and 9.5. Who had the higher average score? Explain.

Understand

1. Circle Dominique's scores.

2. Underline Kim's scores.

3. How many scores did each girl receive? ________

Plan

4. How do you find the average score? ______________________

____

Solve

5. How many points did each girl score in all?

a. Dominique ________ **b.** Kim ________

6. What was each girl's average score?

a. Dominique ________ **b.** Kim ________

7. Who had the higher average score? Explain. ______________________

____

Look Back

8. How could you find who had the higher average without doing all the calculations? ______________________

____

____

SOLVE ANOTHER PROBLEM

In an ice skating competition, Alex scored 7.2, 7.5, 7.1, 6.9, and 7.7. Mario scored 7.1, 7.5, 7.8, 7.0, and 6.9. Who had the higher average score? Explain.

____

Name ______________________________

Guided Problem Solving
3-11

Manuel was counting the lights on parade floats. Each float was 36.4 feet long, and they ran bumper to bumper for 5314.4 feet. If there were 150 lights on each float, how many lights did he count?

Understand

1. What are you asked to find? ______________________________

2. Underline the information you need.

Plan

3. How can you find how many floats were in the parade? ______________________________

____

4. Given the number of floats, how can you find the number of lights?

____

____

Solve

5. Write equations showing the number of floats and lights on floats in the parade.

a. Floats ______________________ **b.** Lights ______________________

6. How many lights did Manuel count? ______________

Look Back

7. How could you use the strategy, Solve a Simpler Problem, to find the number of lights? ______________________________

____

____

SOLVE ANOTHER PROBLEM

Cybill was counting the lights on her neighbor's fence. Each section of the fence was 6.2 feet long, and the fence was 210.8 feet long. If there were 25 lights on each section, how many lights did she count?

____

Name ______________________________

Guided Problem Solving
3-12

A wagon weighs 165.3 kg. Carrying riders, the wagon weighs 465 kg. What is the weight of the riders?

Understand

1. How much does the empty wagon weigh? __________

2. How much does the wagon with riders weigh? __________

Plan

3. Which operation will you use to find the weight of the riders? ______________

4. Which number sentence would be a good estimate for the weight of the riders? ______

a. 500 − 200 = 300   **b.** 500 × 200 = 1000   **c.** 500 + 200 = 700

Solve

5. How much more does the wagon carrying riders weigh than the empty wagon? __________

6. Write a sentence that gives the weight of the riders. ______________________

____

Look Back

7. Compare the weight you found in Item 5 to your estimate in Item 4. How can you use these two answers to see if your answer is correct? ______________________

____

____

____

8. Show another way to check your answer. ______________________

SOLVE ANOTHER PROBLEM

A dog weighs 84.8 kg. Carrying a backpack filled with some cans of food, the dog weighs about 100 kg. What is the weight of the cans of food? ______________________

Name ________________________________

Guided Problem Solving
4-1

Kristin wants to put organic garbage in a compost pile. She staked out a triangular area on the ground that has two sides of 6 and 8 feet. If the perimeter of the pile is 21 feet, how long is the third side?

Understand

1. What are you asked to find? ________________

2. What are the lengths of two of the sides? ________________

3. What is the perimeter? ________________

4. How do you find the perimeter of a triangle? ________________

Plan

5. Write an addition equation to help you solve the problem. Let s = the length of the side you do not know. ________________

6. Which of the following is a reasonable range for the length of the third side? ________

   a. Less than 5 feet **b.** Between 5 and 10 feet **c.** More than 10 feet

Solve

7. Solve the equation. What is the length of the unknown side? ________________

8. Write a sentence describing the size and shape of the compost pile. ________________

____

____

Look Back

9. Write a subtraction equation that you could use to find the length of the third side. ________________

SOLVE ANOTHER PROBLEM

Kristin staked out a rectangular area on the ground that has one side measuring 6 feet. If the perimeter of the pile is 28 feet, how long are the other sides?

____

Name ______________________________

Guided Problem Solving
4-2

Robert and his granddaughter Bailey built a playhouse. The foundation of the playhouse was a 1.86 m-by-95 cm rectangle. What was the perimeter of Bailey's playhouse? Explain.

Understand

1. What are you asked to find? ______________________________

2. What size and shape is the foundation? ______________________________

3. How would you find the perimeter of the foundation?

____

____

Plan

4. Both dimensions should be in the same unit.
What will you do to convert meters to centimeters? ______________________________

5. How many centimeters equal 1.86 meters? ______________________________

Solve

6. Find the perimeter of the foundation in centimeters. ______________________________

7. Explain. How did you find your answer? ______________________________

____

____

Look Back

8. What is another way you could find the perimeter of the playhouse? ______________________________

____

____

SOLVE ANOTHER PROBLEM

Allan and Yolanda built a bookcase. The base of the bookcase was a 1.5 m-by-62 cm rectangle. What was the perimeter of their bookcase? Explain.

____

Name ______________________________

Guided Problem Solving
4-3

Patti made this drawing to help her remember the conversion factor for quarts and gallons.

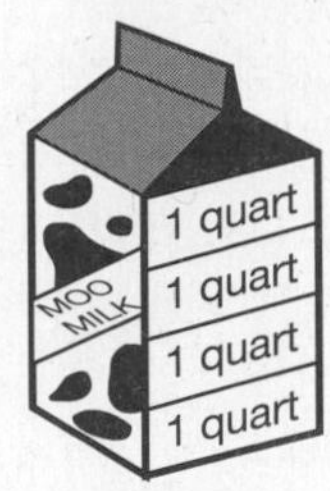

1 gallon

a. How many quarts are in a gallon?

b. How many quarts are in 4 gallons?

c. How many gallons are in 32 quarts?

Understand

1. How many conversions are you asked to make? ______________

2. What information is given in the drawing? ______________

Plan

3. Will you multiply or divide to convert quarts to gallons? ______________

4. Will you multiply or divide to convert gallons to quarts? ______________

5. By which number will you multiply or divide by? ______

Solve

6. Use your answers to Items 3, 4, and 5.

a. How many quarts are in a gallon? ______________

b. How many quarts are in 4 gallons? ______________

c. How many gallons are in 32 quarts? ______________

Look Back

7. How could you have found the answer with a different method? ______________

____

SOLVE ANOTHER PROBLEM

Curtis made this drawing to help him remember the conversion factor for ounces and pounds.

1 ounce	1 ounce
1 ounce	1 ounce
1 ounce	1 ounce
1 ounce	1 ounce
1 ounce	1 ounce
1 ounce	1 ounce
1 ounce	1 ounce
1 ounce	1 ounce

1 pound

a. How many ounces are in a pound? ______________

b. How many ounces are in 8 pounds? ______________

c. How many pounds are in 176 ounces? ______________

Name ______________________________

Guided Problem Solving 4-4

The perimeter of a rectangular bookstore is 220 ft, and its length is 50 ft. What is the annual rent for the bookstore if the rent is $20 per square foot each year? Explain.

Understand

1. Circle the perimeter, length, and annual rent of the bookstore.
2. The rent is per square foot. How do you find the number of square feet in a rectangular figure? ______________________________

Plan

3. You are given the length of one side of the bookstore. What is the length of the opposite side of the bookstore? __________
4. Given the perimeter, how can you use the length of two opposite sides to find the width of the other two sides in a rectangle? __________
____
5. What is the width of the bookstore? __________
6. What operation will you use to find the annual rent? ______________________________

Solve

7. Write a number sentence to find the number of square feet. ______________________________
8. Find the annual rent for the bookstore. __________
9. Explain why it was necessary to follow the steps above. ______________________________
____

Look Back

10. Explain how drawing a diagram could help you solve this problem.
____
____

SOLVE ANOTHER PROBLEM

The perimeter of a rectangular bookstore is 180 ft, and its length is 50 ft. What is the annual rent for the bookstore if the rent is $25 per square foot each year? Explain.

____

Name ______________________________

Guided Problem Solving
4-5

Jaspar drew a parallelogram with a base of 2 cm and a height of 2 cm. He drew another with base 2 cm and height 4 cm and a third with base 2 cm and height 8 cm. If Jaspar continues drawing parallelograms in this pattern, what will the area of the sixth shape be?

Understand

1. Circle the information you need.
2. You are to find the area of the parallelogram in the __________ place in the pattern.
3. What is the formula for finding the area of a parallelogram? ______________________

Plan

4. Draw a picture of the three shapes in the pattern. Label each base and height.

5. What pattern do you see? ______________________

____

Solve

6. What are the measures of the base and height of the sixth parallelogram? ______________
7. What is the area of the sixth parallelogram? __________

Look Back

8. What other strategy could you use to find the pattern? ______________

____

SOLVE ANOTHER PROBLEM

Toi drew a parallelogram with a base of 3 cm and a height of 2 cm. She drew another with base 4 cm and height 3 cm and a third with base 5 cm and height 4 cm. If Toi continues drawing parallelograms in this pattern, what will the area of the seventh shape be? __________

Name ______________________________

Guided Problem Solving
4-6

The Bermuda Triangle is a region in the Atlantic Ocean where ships and airplanes are reported to have mysteriously disappeared since the 1940's. Use the diagram to find the area of the Bermuda Triangle.

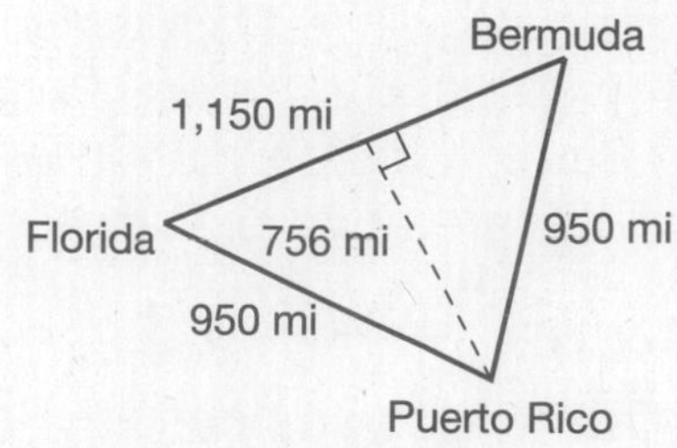

Understand

1. What are you asked to find? ______________________________
2. Circle the information in the picture which will help you solve the problem.

Plan

3. What is the formula for finding the area of a triangle? ______________
4. **a.** What is the base of the Bermuda Triangle? ____________

   b. What is the height of the Bermuda Triangle? ____________
5. Which of the following is a reasonable answer? ________

   a. About 200,000 mi^2 **b.** About 400,000 mi^2 **c.** About 800,000 mi^2

Solve

6. Substitute the values for base and height in the formula.

   ________ × ________ ÷ ________ = ________
7. Write a sentence stating the area of the Bermuda Triangle. ______________

   ____

Look Back

8. Why did you write your answer in square miles? ______________

   ____

SOLVE ANOTHER PROBLEM

Find the area of the triangle.

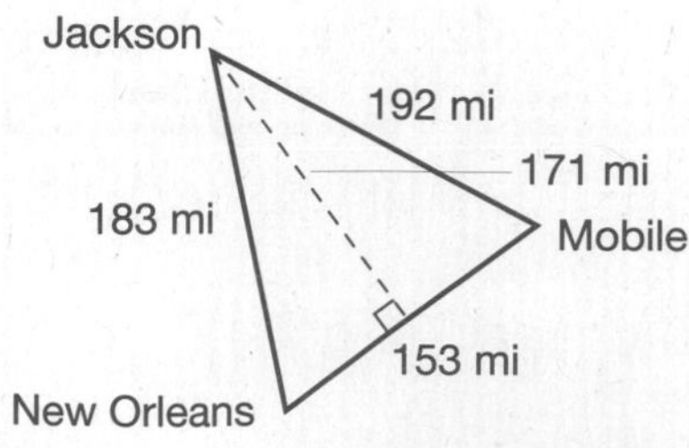

____

Name ______________________________

Guided Problem Solving
4-7

Pat's bicycle has a wheel of radius 13 inches. If she rides the bicycle 1 mile (63,360 inches), how many times has the wheel rotated? Explain.

Understand

1. What are you asked to find? ______________________________

2. The ____________ of the bicycle wheel is the same as one rotation of the wheel.

3. What is the value of pi? ____________

4. Circle the information you need.

Plan

5. What is the diameter of the wheel? ____________

6. What is the circumference of the wheel? ____________

7. Write an expression for the number of rotations. ____________

Solve

8. How many times does the wheel rotate? ____________

9. Explain how you can find the answer. ______________________________

____

____

Look Back

10. How could you find the number of rotations only using division? ____________

____

SOLVE ANOTHER PROBLEM

If the radius of Pat's bicycle wheel were 15 inches and she rode her bicycle for 2 miles, how many times would the wheel rotate? Explain.

____

____

Name ____________________

Guided Problem Solving
4-8

A sand dollar is an animal that lives slightly buried in the sand of shallow coastal waters. Its thin, circular body is about 2 to 4 inches wide. What are the smallest and largest areas of sand dollars?

Understand

1. Which mathematical term describes the "width" of a circle? ____________

2. You need to find the area of how many sand dollars? ____________

Plan

3. What is the formula for finding the area of a circle? ____________

4. To convert diameter to radius, you divide the diameter by ________.

5. What is the value of pi to the nearest hundredth? ________

Solve

6. What is the radius of the smallest sand dollar? ____________

   Substitute the values of the radius and pi in the formula for finding area of a circle.

   ________ × ________ = ________

7. What is the area of the smallest sand dollar? ____________

8. What is the radius of the largest sand dollar? ____________

   Substitute the values of the radius and pi in the formula for finding area of a circle.

   ________ × ________ = ________

9. What is the area of the largest sand dollar? ____________

Look Back

10. How could you estimate to see if your answer is reasonable? ____________

____

SOLVE ANOTHER PROBLEM

What is the area of a sand dollar that has a circular body that is 3 inches wide? ____________

Name ______________________________

Guided Problem Solving
4-9

Sheetal is painting a cardboard cutout for her school's annual play. The cardboard is a triangle 7 feet tall and 7 feet wide. It has a square opening as shown. How many square feet does Sheetal need to paint? Explain your reasoning.

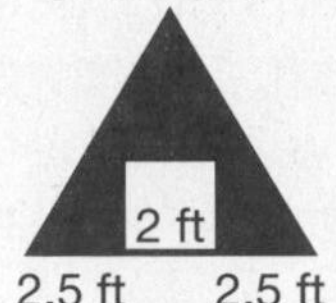

Understand

1. What are you asked to find? ______________________________
2. Underline the measurements of the triangle's height and width.

Plan

3. What is the formula for the area of the triangle? ______________________________
4. What is the formula for the area of the square? ______________________________
5. Will you add or subtract to find the area to be painted? ______________

Solve

6. What is the area of the triangle? ____________ Of the square? ____________
7. Write a number sentence to show how to find the painted area.

____

8. How many square feet will Sheetal paint? Explain. ______________________________

____

Look Back

9. Draw an example of what the cardboard might look like if Sheetal needed to paint the combined areas of the square and the triangle. ______________________________

SOLVE ANOTHER PROBLEM

Liam is painting a cardboard cutout. The cardboard is a square with 8-ft sides, and it has a circular opening as shown. About how many square feet does Liam need to paint? Explain your reasoning.

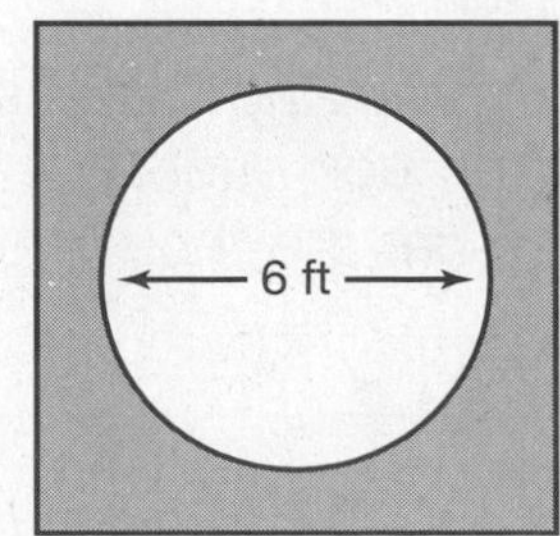

____

Name ______________________________

Guided Problem Solving
5-1

Marvel Models produces 53,716 model cars each month. They want to design shipping cartons that hold more than 3 but fewer than 10 models each. They want to pack each month's cars in their cartons, with no cars left over. What are their choices? Explain.

Understand

1. Underline what you are asked to find.
2. Circle the information you need.

Plan

3. To find which carton sizes to use for shipping, use divisibility rules or division to test 53,716 for divisibility by 4, 5, 6, 7, 8, and 9. If 53,716 is evenly divisible by the carton size, then all the models can be shipped using that sized carton.

   Is 53,716 evenly divisible

   a. by 4? ________ **b.** by 5? ________ **c.** by 6? ________

   d. by 7? ________ **e.** by 8? ________ **f.** by 9? ________

Solve

4. Which number is 53,716 evenly divisible by? ________
5. Write a sentence to tell which size cartons can be used by Marvel Models.

   ____

Look Back

6. How do you know that you checked all the possible carton sizes given in the problem?

   ____

   ____

SOLVE ANOTHER PROBLEM

The Pool Company is shipping 5325 wading pools. They want to design shipping cartons that hold 2, 3, 5, 6, 9, or 10 pools each. They want to pack each month's pools in their cartons with no pools left over. What are their choices? Explain.

____

____

Name ____________________

Guided Problem Solving
5-2

Mr. Armond has 36 students in his math class. He wants to put them into groups of the same size. He also wants the number in each group to be a prime factor of 36. What are his choices?

Understand

1. What are you asked to find?

____

____

Plan

2. To find the possible group sizes, find the prime factors of 36.

Complete the factor tree to find the prime factors.

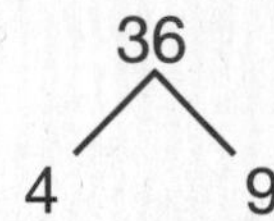

36 = ______ × ______ × ______ × ______

Solve

3. Which numbers are the prime factors of 36? ______

4. Write a sentence to tell how many students could be in each group.

____

Look Back

5. How could you have found the answer using another method?

____

____

SOLVE ANOTHER PROBLEM

Cassie is lining up 45 students in the pep squad. She wants each row to have the same number of students. She also wants the number of students in each row to be a prime number. What are her options?

____

Name ______________________________

Guided Problem Solving
5-3

In a middle school, the principal plans to hide prizes in the new lockers for the students. The principal plans to put a binder in every 10th locker, a school tee shirt in every in every 15th locker, and a new backpack in every 50th locker. If she starts counting at locker number 1, what is the number of the first locker in which the principal will put all three prizes?

Understand

1. Restate the problem in your own words.

____

____

____

2. Underline the information you need.

Plan

3. Find the least common multiple for 10, 15, and 50.

   a. List multiples of 10:

   ____

   b. List multiples of 15: ______________________________

   c. List multiples of 50: ______________________________

Solve

4. What is the least common multiple of 10, 15, and 50? ________

5. Which will be the first locker to contain a binder, a tee shirt, and a backpack? ______________

Look Back

6. What is another way you could solve the problem?

____

SOLVE ANOTHER PROBLEM

Ernesto, Michelina, and Kale volunteer at the zoo. Ernesto works every 5 days. Michelina works every 6 days. Kale works every 15 days. They work together today. How many days will it be until the next time they work together? ______________

Name ____

Guided Problem Solving
5-4

Name two fractions that describe the number of square picture frames. Identify the numerators and denominators.

Understand

1. What are you asked to do?

____

____

Plan

2. What will the numerator describe? ______________________

3. What will the denominator describe? ______________________

Solve

4. How many picture frames are shaped like squares? __________

5. How many picture frames are there in all? __________

6. What are two fractions that describe the number of square picture frames?

____

7. What are the numerators in the two fractions you wrote? __________

8. What are the denominators in the two fractions you wrote? __________

Look Back

9. What two other equivalent fractions could you write for the number of square picture frames? ______________________

SOLVE ANOTHER PROBLEM

Name two fractions that describe the number of shaded rectangles. One of the fractions should have 10 as the denominator. Identify the numerators and denominators.

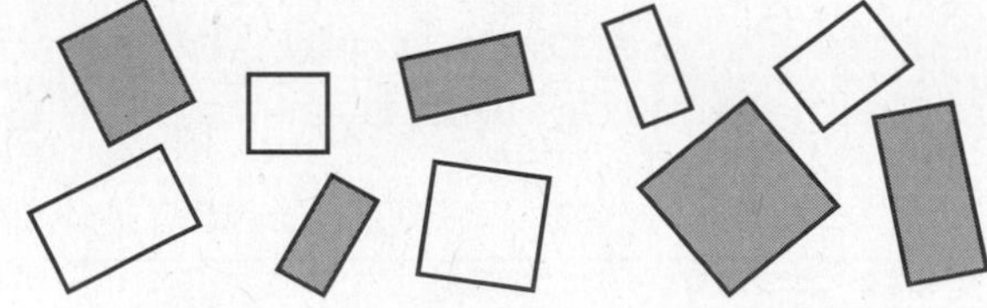

____

Name ______________________________

Guided Problem Solving
5-5

Marilyn sold $\frac{3}{6}$ of the raffle tickets at a carnival. Darren sold $\frac{2}{8}$ of them. Jamelya sold the rest. Who sold more tickets, Marilyn by herself, or Darren and Jamelya together? Explain.

Understand

1. Restate the problem in your own words. ______________________________

____

____

Plan

2. Which strategy could you use to solve the problem? ________

   a. Make a Table **b.** Look for a Pattern **c.** Solve a Simpler Problem

Solve

3. If 6 tickets were sold, how many tickets did Marilyn sell? __________

4. If 6 tickets were sold, how many tickets did Darren and Jamelya sell? __________

5. Compare the number of tickets Marilyn sold to the number of tickets Darren and Jamelya sold. Who sold more tickets? Explain.

____

____

____

Look Back

6. What other strategies could you use to solve the problem?

____

SOLVE ANOTHER PROBLEM

Casey ate $\frac{3}{8}$ of a pizza. Ann ate $\frac{2}{8}$ of the pizza and Juan ate the rest. Who ate more pizza, Juan by himself, or Casey and Ann together?

____

Name ______________________________

Guided Problem Solving
5-6

Caesar has a tool box that is $15\frac{3}{4}$ in. long. His hammer is $\frac{45}{4}$ in. long. Will the hammer fit in the tool box?

Understand

1. What do you need to find?

____

2. Circle the information you need.

Plan

3. For the hammer to fit in the tool box, should the length of the hammer be longer or shorter than the length of the tool box? ____________

4. Write $\frac{45}{4}$ as a mixed number. ________

5. Compare the whole number of the number you wrote in Item 4 with the whole number in $15\frac{3}{4}$. Which is greater? ________

Solve

6. Will the hammer fit in the tool box? Explain how you know.

____

____

____

Look Back

7. Can you think of another way to solve the problem? Explain.

____

____

SOLVE ANOTHER PROBLEM

Yoko has $2\frac{5}{8}$ pounds of trail mix in one bag. Sam has $\frac{10}{8}$ pounds of trail mix in ten bags. Who has more trail mix? Explain how you know.

____

____

Name ______________________________

Guided Problem Solving
5-7

Melissa is using a set of wrenches that come in these sizes: 0.125 inch, 0.25 inch, 0.375 inch, 0.5 inch, 0.625 inch, 0.75 inch, and 0.875 inch. Write each wrench size as a fraction in lowest terms.

Understand

1. What are you asked to find?

____

Plan

2. Write the steps to follow when you write a decimal as a fraction.

____

____

3. Use your rule to write 0.125 as a fraction. ________

4. Find the greatest common factor for the numerator and denominator. ________

Solve

5. Use the greatest common factor to write the fraction in lowest terms. ________

6. Repeat steps 3 through 5 for the remaining decimals.

a. 0.25 ________ **b.** 0.375 ________ **c.** 0.5 ________

d. 0.625 ________ **e.** 0.75 ________ **f.** 0.875 ________

Look Back

7. Check your answers by converting the fractions to decimals. Are the decimals you find the same as the original decimals?

____

____

SOLVE ANOTHER PROBLEM

Timothy bought some salads for a party. The salads weighed 0.6 pound, 0.25 pound, 0.15 pound, and 0.375 pound. Write each weight as a fraction in lowest terms.

____

Name ______________________

Guided Problem Solving
5-8

$\frac{3}{5}$ of the tourists who visit Florida come during the summer. $\frac{3}{10}$ travel to Florida during the winter. During which season does Florida get more tourists?

Understand

1. Underline the question.

2. What fraction of tourists visit Florida in the summer? ________

3. What fraction of tourists visit Florida in the winter? ________

Plan

4. Find a common denominator for $\frac{3}{5}$ and $\frac{3}{10}$. ________

5 Rewrite each fraction using the common denominator. ________

Solve

6. Compare the fractions. Which fraction is greater? ________

7. When do more tourists visit Florida—summer or winter? ________

Look Back

8. How could you have solved the problem in a different way?

____

____

9. Use your answer to the problem to make a generalization. If two fractions have the same numerator, which is the greater fraction?

____

SOLVE ANOTHER PROBLEM

Manny, Anita, and Taylor shared the driving on a trip. Manny drove $\frac{1}{8}$ of the distance. Anita drove $\frac{1}{4}$ of the distance. Did Manny or Anita drive more miles? Explain how you know.

____

Name ______________________________

Guided Problem Solving
6-1

Sandra makes bracelets, necklaces, and chokers using leather string. A bracelet requires $\frac{7}{12}$ ft of string, and a necklace requires $\frac{22}{12}$ ft. She has $\frac{81}{12}$ ft, which is exactly enough to make 3 bracelets, 2 necklaces, and 1 choker. How much string does each choker require? Explain.

Understand

1. Circle what you are asked to find.
2. How much leather string does Sandra have? __________
3. Underline the amount of string needed to make a bracelet and a necklace.

Plan

4. Which operation will you use to find the amount of string needed to make

   3 bracelets? ______________ 2 necklaces? ______________

5. Which operation will you use to find the string left over after making the bracelets and necklaces? ______________

Solve

6. Write a number sentence showing the amount of string needed to make 3 bracelets. ______________________
7. How much string is needed to make 2 necklaces? __________
8. How much string is needed to make 3 bracelets and 2 necklaces? __________
9. How much string will Sandra have left to make one choker? Explain. __________

   ____

   ____

Look Back

10. What other operation could you have used to find the amount of string needed to make 3 bracelets? ______________

SOLVE ANOTHER PROBLEM

Sandra also makes belts. She has $\frac{92}{12}$ feet of string, which is enough to make 2 bracelets, 2 necklaces, and 1 belt. A bracelet requires $\frac{7}{12}$ feet and a necklace requires $\frac{22}{12}$ feet of string. How much string does each belt require? __________

Name ______________________________

Guided Problem Solving
6-2

A recipe for fruit punch calls for $\frac{3}{8}$ of a quart of lemon drink, $\frac{3}{2}$ of a quart of orange juice, $\frac{1}{10}$ of a quart of cranberry juice, and $\frac{3}{4}$ of a quart of soda water. How large a container is needed for the punch? Explain.

Understand

1. Underline the quantity for each ingredient in the punch.

Plan

2. What is the least common denominator for the ingredients? ________

3. Write an equivalent fraction using the least common denominator.

   a. $\frac{3}{8}$ __________ b. $\frac{3}{2}$ __________ c. $\frac{1}{10}$ __________ d. $\frac{3}{4}$ __________

4. Which operation will you use to find the total quantity of punch? __________

5. Which of the following is a reasonable answer? ________

   a. less than 1 qt b. about 1 qt c. more than 1 qt

Solve

6. How much punch does the recipe make? __________

7. Think about how much liquid most pitchers and punch bowls hold. What is a reasonable size container for the punch? Explain. __________

Look Back

8. What should you do if the size container you chose in Item 7 does *not* fall within the range you chose for Item 5? __________

SOLVE ANOTHER PROBLEM

A recipe for party mix calls for $\frac{3}{4}$ of a cup of cereal, $\frac{1}{4}$ of a cup of peanuts, $\frac{5}{8}$ of a cup of pretzels, and $\frac{1}{2}$ of a cup of crackers. How many cups are in the mix? How large a container is needed? Explain. __________

Name ___________________________________

Guided Problem Solving
6-3

The perimeter of the lid to Janice's rectangular jewelry box is $\frac{10}{4}$ of a yard. If the longer sides are $\frac{3}{4}$ of a yard, how long are the shorter sides? Explain.

Understand

1. Circle the perimeter and underline the length of one side of the lid.

2. How do you find the perimeter? ___________________________

Plan

3. Draw a picture of the jewelry box.
Label the longer sides.

4. Write an equation to find the length of the two longer sides. _______________

5. Use your answer to Item 4 to write an equation showing the length of the two shorter sides. _______________

Solve

6. The sum of two fractions equals your answer to Item 5. The denominator of each of the two fractions will be ______.

Use Guess and Check to find each numerator. Each numerator is ______.

7. What is the length of each shorter side? _______________

8. Explain ___________________________________

____

Look Back

9. What is a different way to find the answer? ___________________________

____

SOLVE ANOTHER PROBLEM

The perimeter of the lid to a rectangular box is $\frac{14}{6}$ of a yard. If the longer sides are $\frac{5}{6}$ of a yard, how long are the shorter sides? Explain. _______________

____

Name ______________________________

Guided Problem Solving
6-4

Dimitri lives near the Colorado River. He should evacuate his home when the river reaches 28 feet. The river is now at $21\frac{7}{10}$ feet and is predicted to rise another $6\frac{1}{2}$ feet this evening. Will Dimitri need to evacuate?

Understand

1. Dimitri should evacuate when the river reaches what level? ____________

2. What is the level of the river now? ____________

3. How much is the river predicted to rise this evening? ____________

Plan

4. Will you use addition or subtraction to decide whether or not Dimitri will need to evacuate? ____________

5. To round a mixed number, should you drop the fraction if it is more than $\frac{1}{2}$ or if it is less than $\frac{1}{2}$? ____________

Solve

6. Round the mixed numbers. Write an equation to tell how high the river will be if it rises as much as predicted. ____________

7. Will the river reach 28 feet? ________

8. Write a sentence to tell whether or not Dimitri will need to evacuate. ____________

Look Back

9. Could you draw a picture to help you find the answer? Explain. ____________

SOLVE ANOTHER PROBLEM

Suppose Dimitri will need to evacuate when the river reaches 30 feet. The river is predicted to rise $5\frac{7}{12}$ feet from its present level of $21\frac{7}{10}$ feet. Will he need to evacuate? ____________

Name ______________________

Guided Problem Solving
6-5

The combined area of Shapes A and B is $4\frac{2}{3}$ m^2. The area of Shape B is $1\frac{1}{3}$ m^2 more than the area of Shape A. Find the areas of both shapes.

Understand

1. What are you asked to find? ______________________

2. What is the combined area of the shapes? __________

3. How much larger is Shape B than Shape A? __________

Plan

The diagram represents the combined area of the two shapes. Use the diagram to answer the questions.

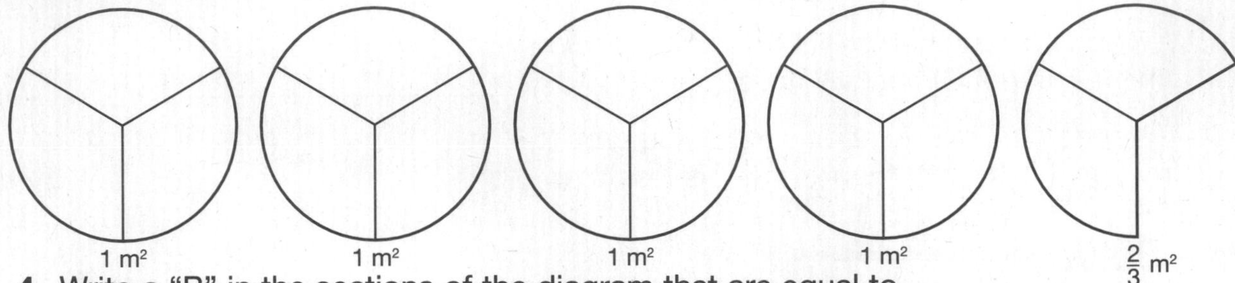

4. Write a "B" in the sections of the diagram that are equal to difference in the areas of Shape B and Shape A.

5. With the difference accounted for, the area of Shape A equals the area of Shape B. Write an "A" for Shape A and a "B" for Shape B in the remaining sections.

Solve

6. Use the sections labeled "A" in the diagram to write the area of Shape A. __________

7. Use the sections labeled "B" in the diagram to write the area of Shape B. __________

Look Back

8. Write and solve an addition equation to check your answer.

____

SOLVE ANOTHER PROBLEM

The combined area of Shapes C and D is $8\frac{3}{4}$ in^2. The area of Shape D is $2\frac{1}{4}$ in^2 more than the area of Shape C. Find the areas of both shapes.

____

Name ________________________________

Guided Problem Solving
6-6

A large financial institution trading on the New York Stock Exchange listed its highest selling price in the last year at $80\frac{3}{8}$ points. The difference between its highest and lowest prices was $26\frac{1}{2}$ points. Write and solve an equation to find the lowest selling price.

Understand

1. What is the highest selling price of the stock? ____________

2. What is the difference between its highest and lowest prices? ____________

Plan

3. What is the least common denominator for $\frac{3}{8}$ and $\frac{1}{2}$? ________

4. Write the prices using the least common denominator.

   a. Highest selling price ________ b. Difference in selling price ________

5. Which operation will you use to find the difference? ____________

6. When you write the equation, which variable will you use to represent the value of the lowest selling price of the stock? ____________

Solve

7. Write an equation to find the lowest selling price. ____________

8. Solve the equation. What is the lowest selling price? ____________

Look Back

9. Write an equation that will find the lowest selling price using another operation.

____

SOLVE ANOTHER PROBLEM

The highest selling price of the stock was $75\frac{3}{4}$. The difference between its highest and lowest prices was $18\frac{1}{8}$. Write and solve an equation to find the lowest selling price.

____

Name ______________________________

Guided Problem Solving
7-1

Give five pairs of values for x and y so that $5\frac{x}{y}$ will round to 6 when rounded to the nearest whole number. What do all of your pairs of numbers have in common?

Understand

1. Which whole number are you asked to round $5\frac{x}{y}$ to? ________

Plan

2. Will you round $5\frac{x}{y}$ up or down? ________
3. If a fraction is less than $\frac{1}{2}$ will you round up or down to the nearest whole number? ________________
4. Will the fractional part of $5\frac{x}{y}$ be less than or greater than or equal to $\frac{1}{2}$? ______________________________

Solve

5. Complete the table. Give five pairs of values for x and y so that $5\frac{x}{y}$ will round to 6.

x					
y					

6. What do all the pairs of numbers have in common?

____

____

Look Back

7. Why did you decide whether to round $5\frac{x}{y}$ up or down before deciding on values for x and y? ______________________

____

____

SOLVE ANOTHER PROBLEM

Complete the table. Give five pairs of values for x and y so that $5\frac{x}{y}$ will round to 5 when rounded to the nearest whole number. What do all of your pairs of numbers have in common?

x					
y					

____

____

Name ______________________________

Guided Problem Solving
7-2

Castile soap is named for the kingdom of Castile in Spain where the soap was first produced. To make about 36 bars, 1 pound 9 ounces of olive oil is needed. If a pound of olive oil costs $8.00, how much does the olive oil for this recipe cost? Explain.

Understand

1. Underline what you are asked to find.
2. What is the cost per pound of the olive oil? __________
3. How much olive oil is used to make 36 bars of soap? ______________________

Plan

4. There are 16 ounces in one pound. How many ounces of olive oil are used to make 36 bars of soap? _________________
5. Write the quantity of olive oil as an improper fraction. _______
6. Write an expression to show how to find the cost of the olive oil used in 36 bars of Castile soap. __________

Solve

7. What is the cost to make 36 bars of soap?. __________
8. Explain how you found the answer. ______________________________

____

____

Look Back

9. How could you find your answer in a different way? ______________________

____

____

SOLVE ANOTHER PROBLEM

To make about 72 bars, 3 pounds 2 ounces of olive oil is needed. If a pound of olive oil costs $9.00, how much does the olive oil for this recipe cost? Round your answer to the nearest cent. Explain.

____

Name ____________________

Guided Problem Solving 7-3

To make $\frac{3}{4}$ cup of powdered-milk paint, you mix $\frac{1}{2}$ cup of powdered nonfat milk and $\frac{1}{2}$ cup of water. Adjust this recipe to make one whole cup of paint. Explain your method.

Understand

1. Circle the quantity of paint that is made from the recipe.
2. Underline the quantities of the paint ingredients.

Plan

3. How many fourths are in $\frac{3}{4}$? ____________
4. To rewrite the recipe for $\frac{1}{4}$ cup of paint, you could divide each quantity by the number in Item 3 or multiply by ________.
5. Once the recipe has been written for $\frac{1}{4}$ cup of paint, you can rewrite it for 1 cup of paint by multiplying each quantity by ________.

Solve

6. Complete the table for $\frac{1}{4}$ cup of paint. Then use your answer to find the quantities for 1 cup of paint.

Paint (cups)	Milk (cups)	Water (cups)
$\frac{3}{4}$	$\frac{1}{2}$	$\frac{1}{2}$
$\frac{1}{4}$		
1		

7. Explain how you found the quantities.

____

____

Look Back

8. Explain how you could use division to rewrite the recipe. ____________________

____

SOLVE ANOTHER PROBLEM

To make $\frac{3}{4}$ cup of powdered-milk paint, you mix $\frac{1}{2}$ cup of powdered nonfat milk and $\frac{1}{2}$ cup of water. Adjust this recipe to make $1\frac{1}{8}$ cup of paint. Explain your method. ____________________

____

Name ______________________

Guided Problem Solving
7-4

As a result of the 1990 census, Pennsylvania has 21 seats in the House of Representatives. This is $\frac{7}{10}$ as many seats as Texas has. How many seats does Texas have?

Understand

1. Underline what you are asked to find.
2. How many seats did Pennsylvania have as a result of the 1990 census? __________
3. The number of Representatives from Pennsylvania is what fraction of the number of Representatives from Texas? ______

Plan

4. Will Texas have fewer or more Representatives than Pennsylvania? __________
5. Which operation will you use to find the number of seats Texas has in the House of Representatives? __________
6. Which would be a reasonable number of seats for Texas to have in the House of Representatives? ______

   a. 15 seats **b.** 21 seats **c.** 30 seats

Solve

7. Write an equation showing the number of seats Texas has in the House of Representatives. ________
8. How many seats does Texas have? __________

Look Back

9. How could you use decimals to find your answer? ______________________

____

____

SOLVE ANOTHER PROBLEM

As a result of the 1990 census, Colorado has 6 seats in the House of Representatives. This is $\frac{3}{10}$ as many seats as Illinois has. How many seats does Illinois have? __________

Name ____________________

Guided Problem Solving 7-5

The size of letters in printed material such as newspapers or books is measured in points. One point equals $\frac{1}{72}$ of an inch.

a. What is the point size of type that is $\frac{1}{8}$ of an inch high?

b. What is the point size of type that is $1\frac{1}{2}$ inches high?

Understand

1. What part of an inch is equal to one point? ____________________

2. What are you asked to find? ____________________

____

Plan

3. Will each type size be more than or less than 72 points?

a. $\frac{1}{8}$ inch type ____________________

b. $1\frac{1}{2}$ inches ____________________

4. Write $1\frac{1}{2}$ as an improper fraction. ________

5. Write an expression to show how to use division to find each point size.

a. $\frac{1}{8}$ inch type ____________________

b. $1\frac{1}{2}$ inches ____________________

Solve

6. Simplify your expressions to find the number of points in each.

a. $\frac{1}{8}$ inch type ____________________ **b.** $1\frac{1}{2}$ inches ____________________

Look Back

7. How can you use multiplication to check your answer? ____________________

____

SOLVE ANOTHER PROBLEM

What is the point size of type that is $\frac{1}{6}$ of an inch? ____________________

Name ______________________________

Guided Problem Solving 7-6

Length was once measured in palms and spans. One inch equaled $\frac{1}{3}$ of a palm and $\frac{1}{9}$ of a span.

a. Which equation could you use to find the number of palms in 12 inches?

A $p \div \frac{1}{3} = 12$ **B** $\frac{1}{3}p = 12$

b. How many palms are in 12 inches?

c. Write and solve an equation to find the number of spans in 18 inches.

Understand

1. How many palms equal one inch? __________ How many spans? __________

Plan

2. In division, you break down a given amount into equal parts. In multiplication, you find how many items in all. Which operation will you use to find how many

a. palms are in 12 inches? **b.** spans are in 18 inches?

__________ __________

3. How are the equations used to find the number of palms in 12 inches and the number of spans in 18 inches similar? __________

____

Solve

4. Which equation would you use to find the number of palms? ________

5. How many palms are in 12 inches? __________

6. Write an equation to find the number of spans in 18 inches. __________

7. How many spans are in 18 inches? __________

Look Back

8. How can you check your answer? ______________________________

____

SOLVE ANOTHER PROBLEM

Write and solve an equation to find the number of inches in 16 palms.

____

Name ______________________________

Guided Problem Solving
8-1

Choose the lines that are parallel.

(A) *A* and *D* (B) *C* and *E*

(C) *A* and *C* (D) *E* and *D*

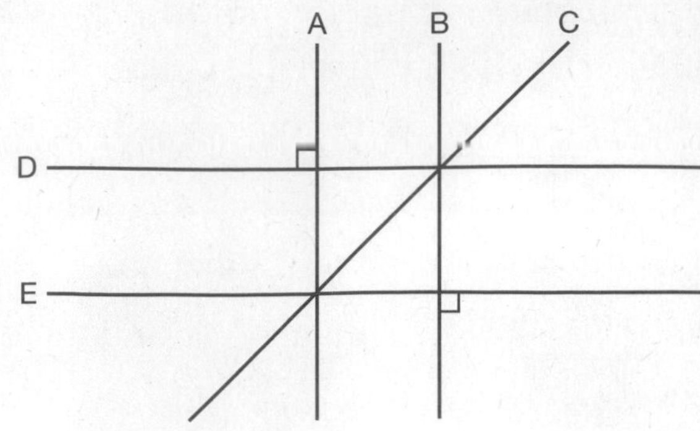

Understand

1. What are you asked to do? ______________________________

2. Do parallel lines intersect? ________

Plan

3. Circle all pairs of parallel lines in the diagram.

4. How many pairs of parallel lines did you circle? ______________

Solve

5. Write the letters of all the pairs of parallel lines. ______________________

6. Compare your answer to Item 5 with the given answer choices.

a Choice (A) says lines A and D are parallel. Is that correct? ________

b. Choice (B) says lines C and E are parallel. Is that correct? ________

c. Choice (C) says lines A and C are parallel. Is that correct? ________

d. Choice (D) says lines E and D are parallel. Is that correct? ________

7. Which choice—A, B, C, or D—is the correct answer? ______________

Look Back

8. Why are lines A and B not the correct answer? ______________________________

____

SOLVE ANOTHER PROBLEM

Which lines in the diagram above are perpendicular?

____

Name ______________________________

Guided Problem Solving
8-2

Tell whether this statement is always, sometimes, or never true.

Two acute angles of the same size form a right angle.

Understand

1. What part of an index card forms a right angle? ______________

2. Is an acute angle smaller or greater than a right angle? ______________

3. How many acute angles are you asked to find? ______________

4. Are the acute angles the same or different sizes? ______________

Plan

5. Draw a right angle. Then draw a line to divide the right triangle into two angles of the same size.

6. Are the two angles in Item 5 acute angles? ________

7. Draw two acute angles of different sizes. Then use one side of each angle to draw another angle the same size.

First angle   Second angle

8. Do both pairs of acute angles you drew in Item 7 form right angles? Explain. ______________________________

____

Solve

9. Use your answers to Items 6 and 8 to tell whether the statement is always, sometimes, or never true. ______________

Look Back

10. What other strategy could you use to find the answer?

____

SOLVE ANOTHER PROBLEM

Is the statement always, sometimes, or never true:
"Three acute angles of the same size form a straight angle." ______________

Name ______________________________

Guided Problem Solving
8-3

Estimate the measurement of the obtuse angle.

(A) 45° (B) 135°

(C) 90° (D) 270°

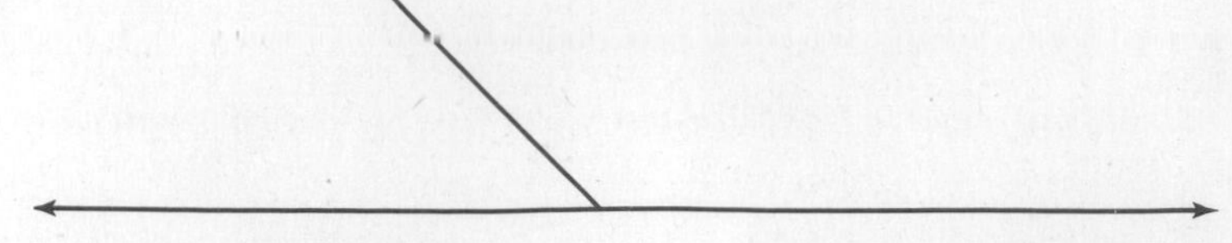

Understand

1. What is the definition of an obtuse angle? ______________________________

____

2. Which of these kinds of angles are shown in the diagram? ________

a. acute and right **b.** right and obtuse **c.** acute and obtuse

Plan

3. Darken the rays that make up the obtuse angle in the diagram.
4. Classify the type of angle given in each choice as acute, obtuse, right, or none of these.

a. Choice A (45°) ______________ **b.** Choice B (135°) ______________

c. Choice C (90°) ______________ **d.** Choice D (270°) ______________

Solve

5. Which choice is an obtuse angle? ______________

Look Back

6. Why does classifying the angle help estimate the measure?

____

____

SOLVE ANOTHER PROBLEM

Which of the answer choices is a reasonable estimate for the measurement of the acute angle in the drawing above? ______________

(A) 45° (B) 135°

(C) 90° (D) 270°

Name ______________________________

Guided Problem Solving
8-4

A triangle has angles *A, B,* and *C.* The complement of $\angle A$ is 58° and the supplement of $\angle B$ is 60°. What is the measure of $\angle C$? Explain your strategy.

Understand

1. Which angle's measurement are you to find? __________

2. Underline the information you need.

Plan

3. What is sum of the measures of two complementary angles? __________

4. The complement of $\angle A$ is 58°. What is the measure of $\angle A$? __________

5. What is sum of the measures of two supplementary angles? __________

6. The supplement of $\angle B$ is 60°. What is the measure of $\angle B$? __________

7. What is sum of the measures of the three angles in a triangle? __________

Solve

8. Add the measurements of $\angle A$ and $\angle B$: __________ + __________ = __________

9. Find the measure of $\angle C$: __________ − __________ = __________

10. What is the measure of $\angle C$? __________

11. What strategy did you use to find the measure of $\angle C$?

____

Look Back

12. What other strategies could you use to find the measure of $\angle C$?

____

____

SOLVE ANOTHER PROBLEM

A triangle has angles *D, E,* and *F.* The complement of $\angle D$ is 42° and the supplement of $\angle E$ is 54°. What is the measure of $\angle F$? __________

Name ______________________________

Guided Problem Solving
8-5

Jeremy has two poles for the end of his tent. They are each 4 feet long. Can he form the triangular end of his tent if he puts two pole ends together and places the other ends 9 feet apart?

Understand

1. What figure will be formed by the two poles and the ground? ______________

2. What are the lengths of each of the two poles? ______________

3. How far apart will Jeremy place the ends of the poles? ______________

Plan

4. Is the sum of the two shorter sides of a triangle greater or less than the length of the longer side? ______________

5. What is the length of the longest side of the figure formed? ______________

6. Write an equation to find the sum of the two shorter tent poles? ______________

Solve

7. Is the sum in Item 6 greater than or less than the length of the longest side? ______________

8. Can Jeremy place the poles 9 feet apart? ________

Look Back

9. What other strategy could you use to find the answer?

____

SOLVE ANOTHER PROBLEM

Diana has two poles for the end of her tent. They are each 8 feet long. Can she form the triangular end of her tent if she puts two pole ends together and places the other ends 10 feet apart? Explain.

____

____

____

____

Name ______________________________

Guided Problem Solving
8-6

The lengths of the sides of a quadrilateral are 3.5 ft, $\frac{7}{2}$ ft, $3\frac{1}{2}$ ft, and $2\frac{3}{2}$ ft. Is the quadrilateral regular or irregular? Explain.

Understand

1. Underline the lengths of the sides of the quadrilateral.
2. Circle what the problem asks you to find.
3. How do you know if a polygon is regular? ______________________________

____

Plan

4. Write each measure as an improper fraction.

   a. 3.5 ________ **b.** $\frac{7}{2}$ ________ **c.** $3\frac{1}{2}$ ________ **d.** $2\frac{3}{2}$ ________

5. Draw a quadrilateral using the given sides and making sure all 4 angles have the same measure. If possible, draw the quadrilateral using the given sides and making sure that all 4 angles do *not* have the same measure.

Solve

6. Is the quadrilateral regular or irregular? Explain. ______________________________

____

____

Look Back

7. What ways could you have written the measures other than as improper fractions?

____

SOLVE ANOTHER PROBLEM

If a pentagon has sides of 2.25 in., $1\frac{5}{4}$ in., $\frac{7}{4}$ in., $2\frac{1}{4}$ in., and 1.75 in., is it regular or irregular? Explain.

____

Name ______________________________

Guided Problem Solving 8-7

Explain why the shape of the kite shown cannot be classified as a trapezoid, a parallelogram, a rhombus, a rectangle, or a square.

Understand

1. Underline the five quadrilaterals that are *not* classifications of the kite.

Plan

2. Which of the five quadrilaterals can be classified as a parallelogram?

____

3. What do you know about the sides of a parallelogram? ______________________________

____

4. What do you know about the sides of the fifth figure? ______________________________

5. Does the kite have any parallel sides? ________

6. Does the kite shape have any pairs of opposite sides that are the same length? ________

Solve

7. Why can a kite not be classified as any of the given quadrilaterals?

____

____

Look Back

8. Does your answer to Item 7 rule out each figure named in the problem? ________

SOLVE ANOTHER PROBLEM

Classify the quadrilaterals that make up the patterns of the kite in as many ways as possible. ______________________________

____

Name ____

Guided Problem Solving 8-8

A triangle has one angle of 40°. The other angles are congruent to each other. What are the measurements of the other two angles? Explain.

Understand

1. What is the measurement of the given angle? ________
2. What does *congruent* mean? ________
3. Would congruent angles have the same or different measures? ________

Plan

4. What is the sum of the measures of the three angles of a triangle? ________
5. Which is a reasonable measure for one of the congruent angles? ________

   a. about 360° **b.** about 180° **c.** less than 90°

Solve

6. Subtract to find the measure of the two congruent angles. ________
7. Write an equation to find the measures of the congruent angles.

   ____

8. What are the measures of the congruent angles? ________

Look Back

9. How could drawing a picture of the triangle help you decide if your answer is reasonable? ________

   ____

   ____

SOLVE ANOTHER PROBLEM

A parallelogram has two pairs of congruent angles. One angle measures 45°. What are the measurements of the other angles? Explain.

____

____

Name ______________________________

Guided Problem Solving
8-9

What is the least number of degrees of rotation that will land the flower on top of itself?

Understand

1. Are you looking at rotational or line symmetry? ______________
2. Do you want to find the greatest or least number of degrees in the rotation? ______________
3. Which is a description of the petals? ________

   a. Congruent **b.** Evenly spaced **c.** Both a and c **d.** Neither a nor b

Plan

4. How many times will the figure "land on itself" when it rotates one complete turn? ______________
5. Are the degrees in each rotation the same or different? ______________
6. How many degrees are in a complete rotation? ________

Solve

7. Complete the equation to find the number of degrees in each rotation.

   ________ ÷ ________ = ________

Look Back

8. Is the degree of rotation greater if the flower is rotated clockwise or counter clockwise?

   ____

SOLVE ANOTHER PROBLEM

What is the least number of degrees of rotation that will land the flower on top of itself?

____

Name ______________________________

Guided Problem Solving
8-10

Draw a tessellation that does not use a polygon as the figure tessellated. Explain your tessellation.

Understand

1. What are you asked to draw? ______________

2. What shape figure are you *not* to use in your drawing? ______________

Plan

3. Can you use all straight line segments in your drawing? Explain. ______________

____

4. Which of the figures below will tessellate? ______________

Solve

5. Choose one of the figures in Item 4 that meets the criteria of Item 3. Then make the drawing.

6. Explain. ______________________________

____

Look Back

7. Draw a different figure to answer the question.

SOLVE ANOTHER PROBLEM

Draw a tessellation that does not use a quadrilateral as the figure tessellated. Explain your tessellation.

____

Name ____________________

Guided Problem Solving
9-1

Order –5, –26, 8, 19, and –20 from least to greatest. Then order these same numbers from closest to zero to furthest from zero. Explain the similarities and differences between your two lists.

Understand

1. Underline the integers you are asked to order.

Plan

2. Show each integer on the number line. Add any necessary labels.

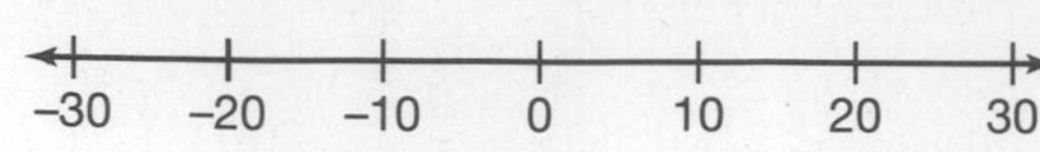

Solve

3. Order the numbers from least to greatest. ____________________

4. The integer +6 is 6 “steps” from zero. So is the integer –6.
   How many “steps” is each of the following integers from zero?

   a. –5 ____________ **b.** –26 ____________ **c.** 8 ____________

   d. 19 ____________ **e.** –20 ____________

5. Use your answers to Item 4 to write the integers in order from closest to zero to furthest from zero. ____________________

6. How are your lists alike? Different? ____________________

____

____

Look Back

7. How could you write the numbers in order from least to greatest without using a number line? ____________________

____

____

SOLVE ANOTHER PROBLEM

Order 12, –3, 5, –14, 19 from least to greatest. Then order these same numbers from closest to zero to furthest from zero.

____

Name ____________________

Guided Problem Solving
9-2

Leon had the following test scores to average: 87, 91, 88, 95, and 89. He said, "I guess my average is about 90. My scores are off that by −3, +1, −2, +5, and −1. When I add those numbers, they add to zero. So I must be right." Do you agree with Leon? Explain.

Understand

1. Underline the test scores.
2. Circle the integers that describe how far each test score is from 90.
3. What did Leon state? ____________________

____

Plan

4. What is the sum of Leon's test scores? ________
5. How many test scores are listed? ________

Solve

6. Divide the sum of the test scores by the number of tests to find the average (mean) test score. ________
7. Is the average of Leon's test scores 90? Do you agree with Leon? ________

Look Back

8. Why might Leon's method *not* be a useful way to find an average? ________

____

____

SOLVE ANOTHER PROBLEM

Ana bowled these scores: 122, 125, 131, and 118. She said, "I guess my average is about 124." Use Leon's method to see if you agree.

____

____

Name ______________________________

Guided Problem Solving
9-3

Nicki visited her dad at work and got lost in the building. She started on the first floor. She rode the elevator up 4 floors, then down 2 floors, then up 6 more floors, then down another floor.

a. Write an expression to represent this situation.

b. If Nicki started on the first floor, which floor did she end up on?

Understand

1. Underline the sentence that describes the floors at which Nicki's elevator stopped.

Plan

2. Draw a diagram of the building. You may wish to use a vertical number line with zero representing the ground floor.

3. Will you use a positive or a negative number to indicate that Nicki rode the elevator *down*?

____

4. Write the integer that represents each part of Nicki's elevator ride.

a. Start on the first floor ________ **b.** Up 4 floors ________

c. down 2 floors ________ **d.** Up 6 floors ________ **e.** Down 1 floor ________

Solve

5. Use the integers in Item 4 to write an expression. ______________________________

6. Simplify your expression to find which floor Nicki ended up on. ________________

Look Back

7. Why was it helpful to draw a diagram? ______________________________

____

SOLVE ANOTHER PROBLEM

Ty climbed one flight of stairs. He then rode the elevator down 2 floors, then up 5 floors, then down 3 more floors, then up another floor.

a. Write an expression to represent this situation. ______________________________

b. If Ty started on the ground floor, which floor did he end up on? ________________

Name ______________________________

Guided Problem Solving
9-4

Sal's business currently has expenses of $4 million and sales of $9 million. Sal wants to triple the size of his business. Express the new expenses, sales, and profit as integers.

Understand

1. What are the current expenses of Sal's business? ______________

2. What are the current sales of Sal's business? ______________

3. What does triple mean? ______________

Plan

4. Tell whether each number will be positive or negative.

   a. Expenses ______________ b. Sales ______________

5. Which operation will you use to triple each amount? ______________

Solve

6. What is triple Sal's current expenses? ______________

7. What is triple Sal's current sales? ______________

8. Profit is the amount remaining after expenses are deducted from sales. Write an equation showing how to find the profit in Sal's business. ______________

Look Back

9. Could you determine if the profit would be a positive or a negative number without doing any calculations? Explain.

____

____

SOLVE ANOTHER PROBLEM

Marky's business currently has expenses of $6 million and sales of $8 million. Marky wants to double the size of her business. Express the new expenses, sales, and profit as integers.

____

____

Name ______________________________

Guided Problem Solving 9-5

Use the map and the directions given to find the coordinates of Smallville School.

The school and the marketplace have the same y-coordinate. The x-coordinate of the school is twice the difference between the y-coordinate of the marketplace and the y-coordinate of the gas station.

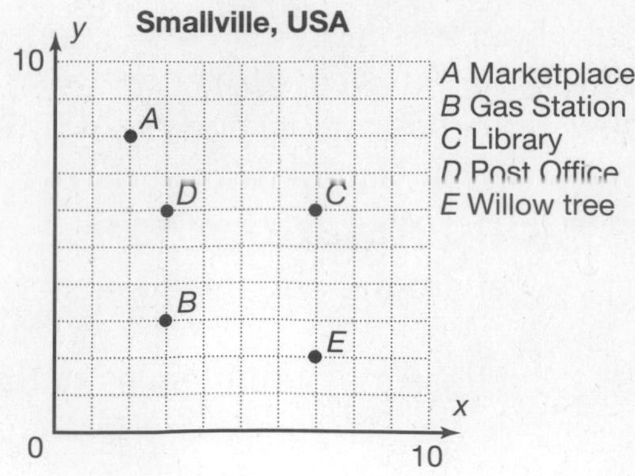

Understand

1. Circle the phrase that tells how to find the y-coordinate of the school.
2. Underline the phrase that tells how to find the x-coordinate of the school.

Plan

3. Which operations will you use to find the x-coordinate of the school? ________

   a. Multiplication, then subtraction **b.** Subtraction, then multiplication

4. The coordinates of the point for the marketplace are ____________
5. The coordinates of the points for gas station are ____________

Solve

6. What is the y-coordinate of the ordered pair in Item 4? ________
7. Use the y-coordinates of the ordered pairs you wrote in Items 4 and 5 to write an equation for the x-coordinate of the school. ________________
8. What are the coordinates of the school? ____________

Look Back

9. Would it have been easier to find the answer by only writing the value of the y-coordinate for each building? Explain. ________________

____

SOLVE ANOTHER PROBLEM

Use the map above and these directions to find the coordinates of the park.

The park and the library have the same x-coordinate. The y-coordinate of the park is one half the sum of the x-coordinate of the post office and the x-coordinate of the library. ____________

Name ______________________________

Guided Problem Solving
9-6

One item that Cheryl had to find on a treasure hunt was located at the point (3, 4) on the map. When Cheryl got there, she realized she had the map upside down. How many units left, right, up, and down on the map should Cheryl walk to find the correct location?

Understand

1. Underline what you are asked to find.

2. Why was Cheryl not at those coordinates? ______________________________

Plan

3. Mark (3, 4) on the coordinate plane. Label it *A*.

4. Turn this page upside down. Imagine that the graph was scaled in the usual way. Then mark (3, 4). Label it *B*.

5. Turn your page to original position. Follow the grid lines to mark the shortest path between the *B* and *A*.

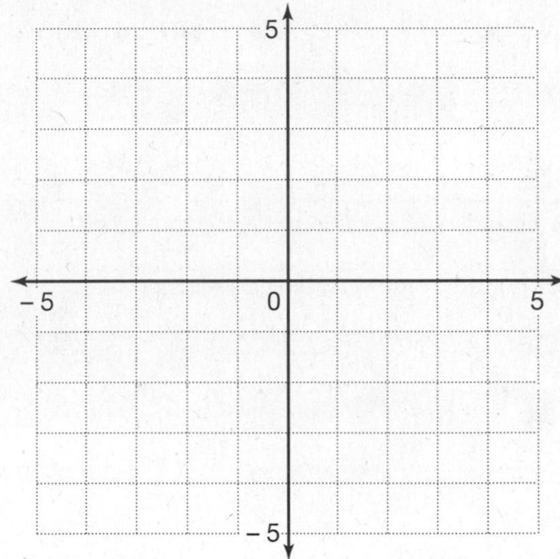

Solve

6. Does your path go up or down? How many units? ______________________________

7. Does your path go left or right? How many units? ______________________________

Look Back

8. Are there other paths that you could choose? Explain. ______________________________

____

9. What is the relationship between the of number of units the path takes and the original coordinates? ______________________________

____

SOLVE ANOTHER PROBLEM

One item that Norm had to find on a treasure hunt was located at the point (–2, 5) on the map. When Norm got there, he realized he had the map upside down. How many units left, right, up, and down on the map should Norm walk to find the correct location? ______________________________

Name ____________________

Guided Problem Solving
9-7

Graph the equations $y = x + 3$ and $y = x + (-3)$ on the same coordinate plane. Describe the relationship between the lines.

Understand

1. Will you graph the equations on one or two coordinates planes? ____________

2. What are you asked to describe? ____________

Plan

3. Complete the T-tables to find some values of x and y for each equation.

$y = x + 3$

x	y
–1	
0	
1	
2	

$y = x + (-3)$

x	y
–1	
0	
1	
2	

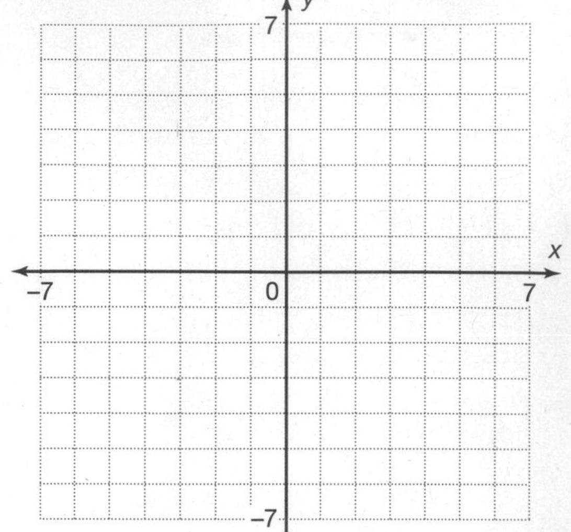

Solve

4. Graph each equation. Label each line.

5. What is the relationship between the lines? ____________

____

Look Back

6. Do you think you would get the same result for the equations $y = x - 3$ and $y = x - (-3)$? Explain. ____________

____

SOLVE ANOTHER PROBLEM

Graph the equations $y = 3x$ and $y = -3x$ on the coordinate plane above. Label each line. Describe the relationship between the lines.

____

____

Name ______________________________

Guided Problem Solving
10-1

Fire engines carry fire hoses. Fire trucks carry mainly ladders and fire-fighting equipment other than hoses. At one point, the city of San Francisco had 40 fire engines and 18 fire trucks.

a. Give the ratio of fire engines to fire trucks in lowest terms.

b. Give the ratio of fire trucks to total fire vehicles in lowest terms.

Understand

1. How many fire *engines* did the city of San Francisco have? ____________

2. How many fire *trucks* did the city of San Francisco have? ____________

Plan

3. How will you find the total number of fire vehicles in San Francisco?

____

4. What is the total number of fire vehicles in San Francisco? ____________

Solve

5. What is the ratio of fire engines to fire trucks? ________

6. Write your ratio in Item 5 in lowest terms, if possible. ________

7. What is the ratio of fire trucks to total fire vehicles? ________

8. Write your ratio in Item 7 in lowest terms, if possible. ________

Look Back

9. How can you tell if the ratio is in lowest terms? ____________________

____

SOLVE ANOTHER PROBLEM

Use the fire vehicle data above to write each ratio in lowest terms.

a. What is the ratio of fire trucks to fire engines? ________

b. What is the ratio of fire vehicles to fire engines? ________

Name ______________________________

Guided Problem Solving
10-2

The circle graph shows the number of colored beads used in a hand-beaded bracelet. Carole wants to make a smaller bracelet using the same ratios of colors. Draw a circle graph that shows how many beads of each color Carole could use.

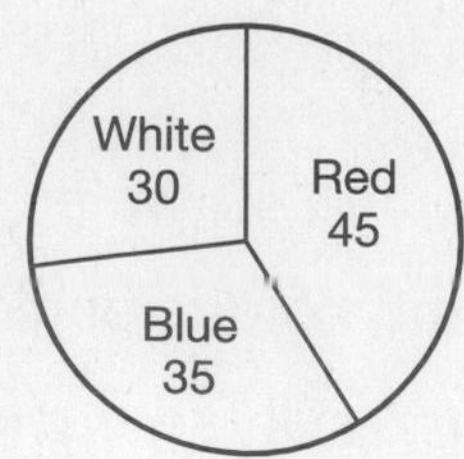

Understand

1. In the circle graph above, how many beads are a. white? ________

b. blue? ________ c. red? ________ d. there in all? ________

Plan

2. Equal ratios can help find the number of beads in the smaller bracelet. Will you multiply or divide to find the equal ratios? ________

3. Write the ratio of blue beads to total beads. Then write an equal ratio. ______ = ______

4. Write each ratio. Then write an equal ratio that has the same number of total beads as the ratio in Item 3.

a. white beads:total beads ________ b. red beads:total beads ________

Solve

5. In the smaller bracelet, how many beads are

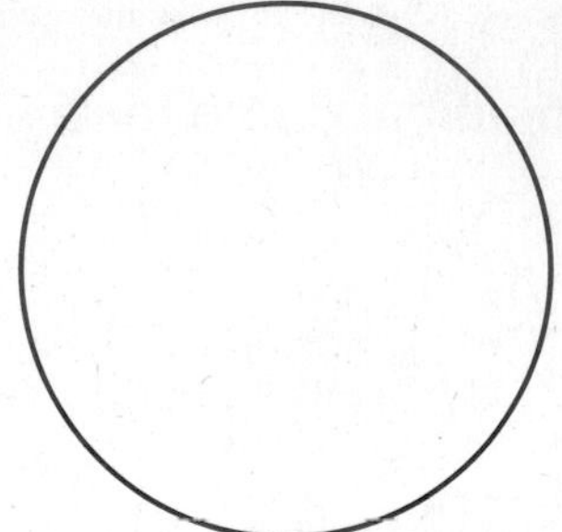

a. there in all? ________ b. white? ________

c. red? ________ d. blue? ________

6. Use your answers to Item 5 to draw a circle graph.

Look Back

7. Did the size of each section in your circle graph change from the size in the graph at the top of the page? Explain. ________

____

SOLVE ANOTHER PROBLEM

Carole wants to make a larger bracelet using the same ratios of colors as in the circle graph at the top of the page. Draw a circle graph that shows how many beads of each color Carole could use.

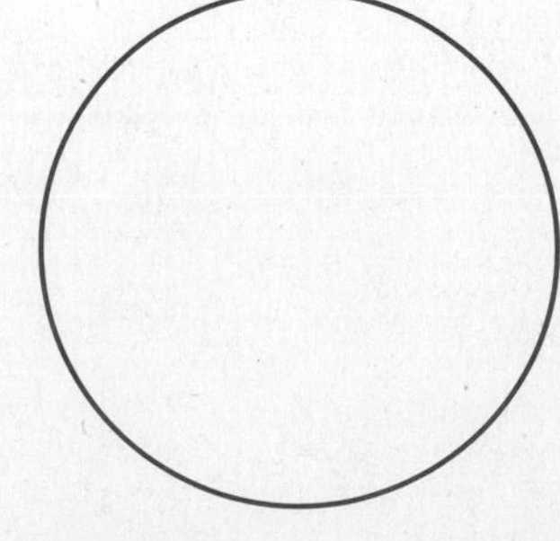

Name ______________________________

Guided Problem Solving
10-3

Cameron is making decorations for "Back to School Night." He can make 2 posters in an hour. At this rate, how long will it take him to make 5 posters? Explain.

Understand

1. Circle how many posters Cameron can make in one hour.
2. Underline what you are asked to find.

Plan

3. What is the unit rate to make the posters? ______________
4. How many minutes in one hour? ______________
5. Write the rate as posters to minutes. ______________
6. Complete the table to find an equal rate.

Posters	1		3		5
Minutes		60		120	

Solve

7. How long will it take Cameron to make 5 posters? ______________
8. How many *hours* will it take Cameron to make 5 posters? ______________
9. Explain how you found your answer. ______________

____

Look Back

10. What is another way to find how long it would take Cameron to make 5 posters? ______________

____

SOLVE ANOTHER PROBLEM

Morgan can make 48 cookies in an hour. At this rate, how long will it take her to make 60 cookies? ______________

Name ______________________________________

Guided Problem Solving
10-4

Janice can run 100 meters in 12 seconds. Carl can run 500 meters in 48 seconds. Susan runs at a rate of 10 meters per second. Phillip can run 200 meters in 24 seconds. Which two students run at the same rate? Explain how you found your answer.

Understand

1. Underline the question.
2. Write the rate that each student runs in meters per seconds.

   a. Janice _____ b. Carl _____ c. Susan _____ d. Phillip _____

Plan

3. Make an organized list to compare the pairs of rates.

   a. Janice and Carl _____ $\stackrel{?}{=}$ _____ b. Janice and Susan _____ $\stackrel{?}{=}$ _____

   c. Janice and Phillip _____ $\stackrel{?}{=}$ _____ d. Carl and Susan _____ $\stackrel{?}{=}$ _____

   e. Carl and Phillip _____ $\stackrel{?}{=}$ _____ f. Susan and Phillip _____ $\stackrel{?}{=}$ _____

Solve

4. Which of the pairs of rates in Item 3 form a proportion? ______________
5. Which students run at the same rate? Explain. ______________________________

____

Look Back

6. How could you find which students run at the same rate by writing each rate in lowest terms. ______________________

____

SOLVE ANOTHER PROBLEM

Guillermo made $15 for baby-sitting 5 hours. Megan made $28 in 8 hours. Thomas earned $2.50 in 1 hour, and Della earned $14 in 4 hours. Which two students were paid the same rate? Explain. ______________

____

Name ______________________________

Guided Problem Solving
10-5

Darius thought that you could solve proportions only when three of the values are given, and one value is missing. Then he saw the proportion $\frac{4}{x} = \frac{x}{9}$, where two values are given and two are missing. Darius was able to solve the problem. What is the value of *x*? Explain your method.

Understand

1. Write the proportion. ____________

2. What are you asked to find? ______________

Plan

3. Use the cross products to write an equation. ______________

Solve

4. Use mental math to find the value of *x*. ______________

5. Explain your method. ____

____

Look Back

6. What other strategy could you use to find the value of *x*? ______________

____

SOLVE ANOTHER PROBLEM

Lorraine saw the proportion $\frac{x}{x} = \frac{x}{9}$, where one value is given and three are missing. Lorraine was able to solve the problem. What is the value of *x*? How can you use this to give the value of *x* for any similar proportions. Explain.

____

____

____

____

Name ______________________________

Guided Problem Solving
10-6

The *Colossi of Memnon* in Karnak, Egypt, are 21 meters tall. They also measure 70 feet tall. Using these measurements, find the number of meters in a foot.

Understand

1. How tall is the *Colossi of Memnon,* in meters? ____________
2. How tall is the *Colossi of Memnon,* in feet? ____________
3. It takes more feet than meters to measure the height. Is a meter longer or shorter than a foot? ____________
4. What are you asked to find? ______________________________

Plan

5. Write the heights as a ratio of meters to feet. ________
6. Complete the equation to find the unit rate.

$$\frac{\text{\_\_ meters} \div \text{\_\_}}{\text{\_\_ feet} \div \text{\_\_}} = \frac{\text{\_\_ meters}}{\text{1 foot}}$$

Solve

7. Write a sentence giving how many meters are in one foot.

____

____

Look Back

8. Let *m* be the number of meters. Use the measurement of the *Colossi* to write a proportion. Then find cross products to solve.

____

SOLVE ANOTHER PROBLEM

A Jamaican pumpkin soup recipe uses 160 milliliters of light cream. This is equal to 32 teaspoons of light cream. Using these measurements, find the number of milliliters in one teaspoon. ____________

Name ______________________________

Guided Problem Solving
10-7

A rectangle has sides of 5 ft and 8 ft. A similar rectangle has two sides of 40 feet. There are two possible answers for the length of the other side of the larger rectangle. What are they?

Understand

1. What are the dimensions of the smaller rectangle? ______________

2. What is one dimension of a similar rectangle? ______________

3. Underline the number of possible answers.

Plan

4. What is true about matching sides of similar figures? ______________________

5. Draw the smaller rectangle. Label the sides.

6. Draw another rectangle. Label the sides so that the 40 ft side matches the 5 ft side.

7. Which other side could the 40 ft side match in the smaller rectangle? ______________

8. Draw the larger rectangle. Label the sides another way.

Solve

9. Write a proportion to find the missing side of the rectangle drawn

   a. in Item 6. __________ b. in Item 8. __________

10. What is the length of the missing side for the rectangle drawn

    a. in Item 6. __________ b. in Item 8. __________

Look Back

11. Why did the two sides measuring 40 feet have to be the parallel sides in the rectangle? ______________________

____

SOLVE ANOTHER PROBLEM

A parallelogram has sides of 2 m and 3 m. A similar parallelogram has two sides of 6 m. There are two possible answers for the length of the other sides of the larger parallelogram. What are they? ______________

Name ______________________________

Guided Problem Solving
10-8

What percent of the shapes are quadrilaterals?

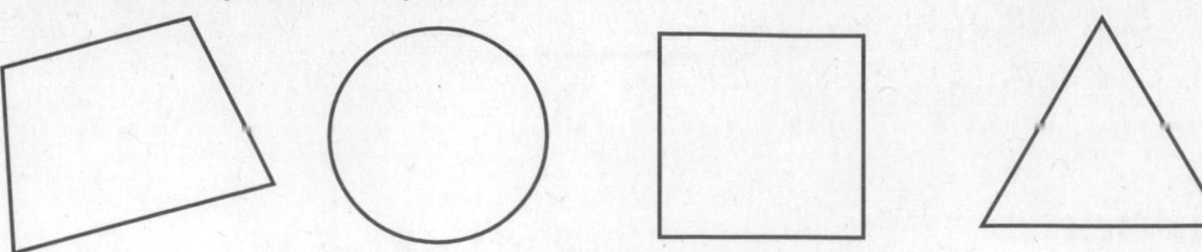

Understand

1. What is the name of the

   a. first figure? ____________ b. second figure? ____________

   c. third figure? ____________ d. fourth figure? ____________

2. What is the definition of a quadrilateral? ____________________

Plan

3. Which of the shapes are quadrilaterals? ____________________

4. Write a ratio of the number of quadrilaterals to the total number of figures. ______

5. A percent compares a part to a whole. What number represents the whole in a percent? ______

Solve

6. Write an equal ratio to the ratio you wrote in Item 4. Use the "whole" you named in Item 5 as the denominator. ______

7. Write the percent of the figures that are quadrilaterals. ______

Look Back

8. What is another way you could find the percent of figures that are quadrilaterals?

   ____

SOLVE ANOTHER PROBLEM

What percent of the shapes are polygons? ______

 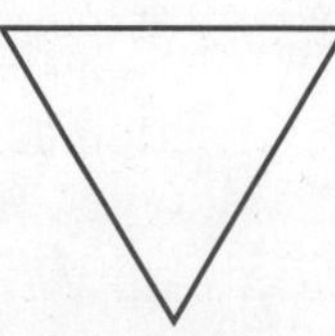 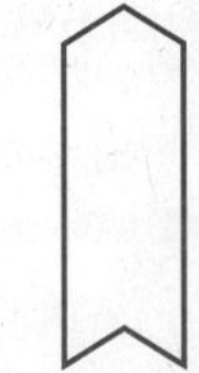 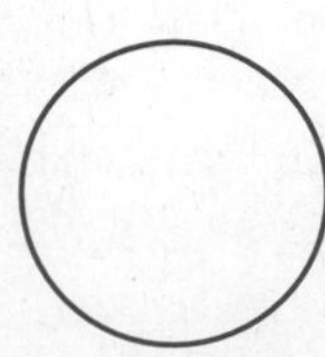

Name ______________________

Guided Problem Solving
10-9

If a shirt was originally $20, went on sale for 15% off, and then was put on clearance with an additional 45% off, estimate the clearance price of the shirt. Explain your reasoning.

Understand

1. What was the original price of the shirt? ________

2. What was the first discount? ________ The second discount? ________

Plan

3. Is 15% closer to $\frac{1}{10}$, $\frac{2}{10}$, or $\frac{1}{4}$? ________

4. Is 45% closer to $\frac{1}{4}$, $\frac{4}{10}$, or $\frac{1}{2}$? ________

Solve

5. Use the fraction in Item 3 to estimate 15% of $20. ________

6. Subtract the discount to find the first clearance price. ________

7. Use the fraction in Item 4 to estimate 45% of the first clearance price. ________

8. Subtract the discount to find the second clearance price. ________

9. Explain your reasoning. ______________________

____

Look Back

10. Do you think your estimated clearance price is higher or lower than the actual clearance price. Explain. ______________________

____

SOLVE ANOTHER PROBLEM

If a jacket was originally $90, went on sale for 30% off, and then was put on clearance with an additional 15% off, estimate the clearance price of the jacket. Explain your reasoning. ______________________

____

Name ______________________

Guided Problem Solving
10-10

45% of the students at Suburban High School are boys. 30% of the boys at Suburban High School have curly hair. What fraction of the students at Suburban High School are boys with curly hair?

Understand

1. What percent of the students at Suburban High are boys? ________

2. What percent of the boys at Suburban High have curly hair? ________

3. Are you going to write your answer as a percent, a decimal, or a fraction? ____________

Plan

4. Suppose you were given the number of boys at Suburban High. How would you find how many boys have curly hair? ________________

____

5. You know the fraction of boys in the school rather than the number of boys. Which operation will you use to find what fraction of students are boys with curly hair? ________________

6. Write the number of students that are boys as a fraction. Then rewrite the fraction in lowest terms. __________

7. Write the number of boys that have curly hair as a fraction. Then rewrite the fraction in lowest terms. __________

Solve

8. Write an expression to find the fraction of students that are boys with curly hair. __________

9. What fraction of the students at Suburban High are boys with curly hair? __________

Look Back

10. Show how to estimate to see if your answer is reasonable. ________________

____

SOLVE ANOTHER PROBLEM

20% of the houses on the block are white. 65% of the white houses have blue trim. What fraction of these houses are white with blue trim? __________

Name ______________________________

Guided Problem Solving
10-11

A new student's score on a spelling test was about 72% of Catherine's score. Catherine's score was about 98% of Tom's score. Tom's score was about 94% of Luanna's score. Luanna got 93 out of 100 points. How many points did the new student get?

Understand

1. How many points did Luanna score on the spelling test? ____________
2. Underline how each student's score relates to another student's score such as, 72% of Catherine's.

Plan

3. Which strategy will you use to find the new student's score? ______

   a. Look for a Pattern **b.** Draw a Diagram **c.** Work Backward

4. What operation do you use to find a percent of a number? ____________
5. There are no fractional points given for partially correct answers. What should you do if your answer is a decimal? ____________

   ____

Solve

6. How many points did Tom score? ____________
7. How many points did Catherine score? ____________
8. How many points did the new student score? ____________

Look Back

9. Order the students scores from least to greatest. Does this correspond with the clues given in the problem? ____________

   ____

SOLVE ANOTHER PROBLEM

Eden's bowling score was about 96% of Remy's score. Remy's score was about 75% of Laneesha's score. Laneesha's score was 100% of Martin's score. Martin's bowling score was 150 points. How many points did the Eden score? ____________

Name ____________________

Guided Problem Solving
11-1

Use what you know about triangular, rectangular, and pentagonal prisms to draw a hexagonal prism. Classify each of the faces and explain your drawing.

Understand

1. What are you asked to draw? ____________________

2. Does a prism have one base or two parallel, congruent bases? ____________

Plan

3. What polygon makes up the base for each of these prisms?

   a. Triangular ____________ b. Rectangular ____________

   c. Pentagonal ____________

4. What polygon will make up the base of a hexagonal prism? ____________

5. What polygon makes up the sides for each of the three given prisms? ____________

6. What polygon will make up the sides of a hexagonal prism? ____________

Solve

7. Draw a hexagonal prism.

8. Explain your drawing.

____

Look Back

9. What is the pattern in the number of faces in triangular, rectangular, and pentagonal prisms? How many faces will be in a hexagonal prism?

____

____

SOLVE ANOTHER PROBLEM

Draw an octagonal prism. Classify each of the faces and explain your drawing?

____

Name ____________________

Guided Problem Solving
11-2

If wrapping paper costs $0.29 a square foot, how much would it cost to cover the box shown?

Understand

1. Underline what you are asked to find.
2. How much does the wrapping paper cost? ____________

Plan

3. How many faces does the box have? ____________
4. What shape is each face? ____________
5. Which net can you use to make the box? ____

a.

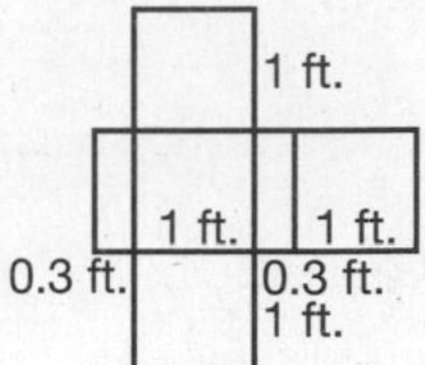

b.

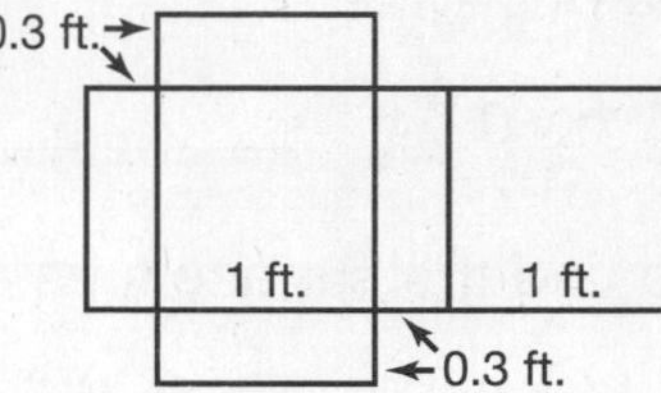

6. Find the area of the top and bottom faces. 2 × ____ × ____ = ____
7. Find the area of the front and back faces. 2 × ____ × ____ = ____
8. Find the area of the left and right faces. 2 × ____ × ____ = ____
9. What is the surface area of the box? ____________

Solve

10. Multiply to find the cost of the paper needed to cover the box without overlapping edges. ____________

Look Back

11. Could you draw a different net for the box? Would it change your answer? Explain.

____

SOLVE ANOTHER PROBLEM

If wrapping paper costs $2.50 a square meter, how much would it cost to cover the box shown? ____

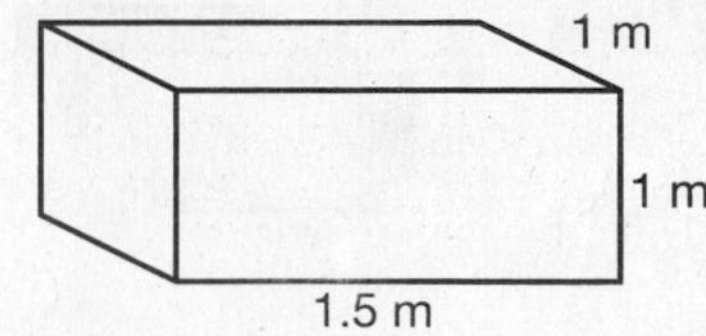

Name ____________________

Guided Problem Solving 11-3

Which solid has the greater surface area? Explain.

a.

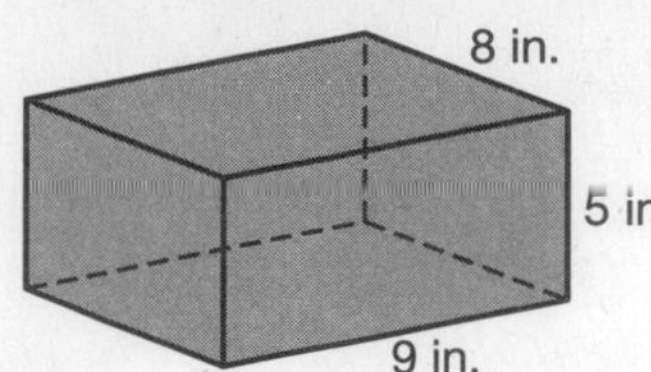

b.

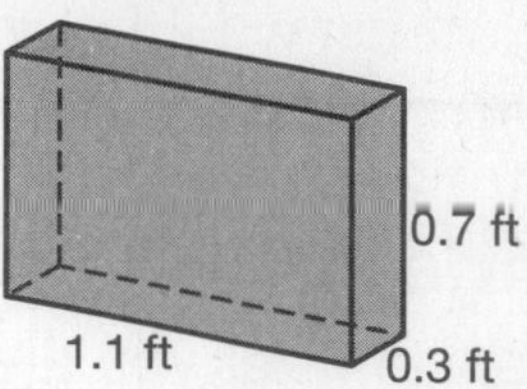

Understand

1. What are you asked to compare? ____________

2. Are the units of measurement the same or different in each solid? ____________

Plan

3. How can you convert feet to inches? ____________

4. Convert each measure to inches.

   a. 1.1 ft ________ **b.** 0.7 ft ________ **c.** 0.3 ft ________

5. What is the formula to find the surface area of each solid? ____

   a. $SA = (2 \times l \times w) + (2 \times l \times h) + (2 \times w \times h)$ **b.** $SA = s^2$

Solve

6. What is the surface area in square inches of Solid a? ____________

7. What is the surface area in square inches of Solid b? ____________

8. Which solid has the greater surface area? Explain.

____

Look Back

9. How could you find the answer in another way? ____________

____

SOLVE ANOTHER PROBLEM

Which solid has the greater surface area? Explain.

a.

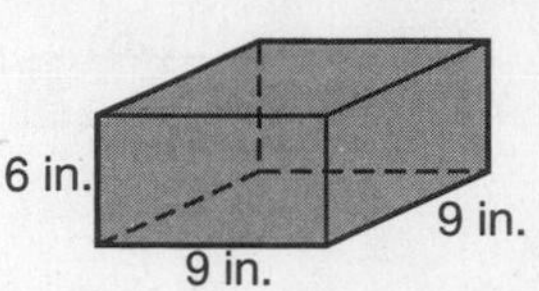

b.

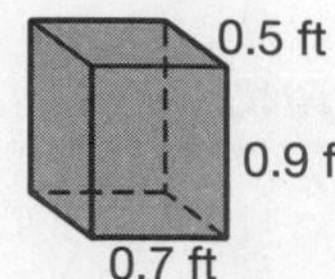

____

Name ______________________________

Guided Problem Solving
11-4

A can of cake frosting is 4.5 inches tall and has a 3 inch diameter.

a. If there is no overlap, what is the area of the can's label?

b. What is the surface area of the entire can?

Understand

1. Underline the height and diameter of the can.

2. Does the side or the base of a can contain the label? ______

Plan

3. What shape is the side of a cylinder? __________

4. What is the formula to find the area of the side of a cylinder? ___

a. $A = 2\pi r^2$ **b.** $A = h \times 2\pi r$ **c.** $A = d\pi$

5. What shape is the base of a cylinder? ________

6. What is the formula to find the area of the base of a cylinder? __________

7. How can you find the total surface area of the can once you know the areas of the base and the side? ______________________

8. What is the radius of the can? ________________

Solve

9. What is the area of the can's label? ________________

10. What is the surface area of the entire can? ________________

Look Back

11. Write the surface area formula. Then use it to check your answer to Item 10.

____

SOLVE ANOTHER PROBLEM

A can is 6.5 inches tall and has a 5 inch diameter.

a. If there is no overlap, what is the area of the can's label? __________

b. What is the surface area of the entire can? ________________

Name ______________________________

Guided Problem Solving
11-5

Describe the pattern.
How many cubes are in the eighth solid of the pattern?

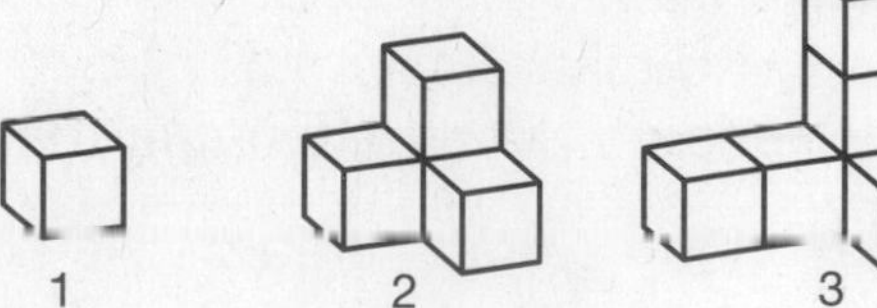

Understand

1. You are asked to find the number of cubes in which place in the pattern? ________

Plan

2. Count the cubes in each figure in the pattern and use this data to complete the table.

Place	1	2	3					
Number of Cubes								

Solve

3. What is the rule for the pattern? ______________

4. Describe the pattern. Include how each figure in the pattern physically changes.

____

____

5. How many cubes are in the eighth solid of the pattern? ______________

Look Back

6. Continue the table to check your answer. What other strategy could you use to check your answer?

____

SOLVE ANOTHER PROBLEM

Describe the pattern.
How many cubes are in the tenth solid of the pattern?

____

Name ______________________________

Guided Problem Solving
11-6

When sugar cubes are produced, they are put into tightly packed boxes for purchasing. If the box of sugar cubes shown is 3 cubes high, how many sugar cubes are in the box?

Understand

1. How many sugar cubes high is the box? ____________

2. What are you asked to find? ____________

Plan

3. How many cubes are in one row? ____________

4. How many cubes are in one column? ____________

5. How many cubes are in one layer? ____________

Solve

6. Complete the number sentence to find the number of sugar cubes in the box. ____ × ____ = ______

7. Write a sentence giving the number of cubes in the box. ____________

____

Look Back

8. Draw a diagram of each layer of sugar cubes. Make sure that the number of cubes matches your answer to Item 6.

SOLVE ANOTHER PROBLEM

Centimeter cubes can be placed in tightly packed boxes. If the box of centimeter cubes shown is 4 cubes high, how many centimeter cubes are in the box?

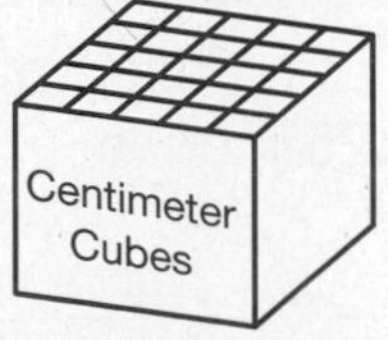

____

Name ______________________________

Guided Problem Solving
11-7

The volume of a gallon of water is about 231 cubic inches. If a 25-gallon aquarium is 32 inches long and 15 inches wide, how deep is it? Explain.

Understand

1. What are you asked to find? ______________________________
2. What is the volume of a gallon of water? ______________________________
3. Underline the dimensions of the aquarium that are given.

Plan

4. How can you find the volume of an aquarium that holds 25 gallons of water? ______________________________
5. What is the volume of the aquarium? ______________________________
6. What is the formula to find the volume of a rectangular prism?

____

7. Substitute known values into the equation you wrote in Item 6.

____

Solve

8. Multiply values in the equation. ______________________________
9. Use mental math, or guess and check to find the depth of the aquarium to the nearest whole number. ______________
10. How deep is the aquarium? Explain. ______________________________

____

Look Back

11. Estimate to see if your answer is reasonable. ______________________________

____

SOLVE ANOTHER PROBLEM

The volume of a gallon of water is about 231 cubic inches. If a 30-gallon aquarium is 25 inches long and 25 inches wide, how deep is it? Explain.

____

Name ______________________________

Guided Problem Solving
12-1

Suppose you roll a number cube. Find P(even number).

Understand

1. What does the problem ask you to find?

____

Plan

2. How many numbers are on a number cube? __________

3. How many possible outcomes are there when you roll a number cube? __________

4. What are the even numbers on a number cube? __________

5. How many ways can you roll an even number? __________

Solve

6. Write the probability of rolling an even number. Which ratio will you use? __________

   a. $P(\text{event}) = \dfrac{\text{number of ways event can happen}}{\text{number of possible outcomes}}$

   b. $P(\text{event}) = \dfrac{\text{number of possible outcomes}}{\text{number of ways event can happen}}$

7. Write the probability. ______________________________

Look Back

7. Are all the possible outcomes equally likely? How do you know?

____

SOLVE ANOTHER PROBLEM

Suppose you toss a twelve-sided number cube with numbers 1-12 on its faces. What is the probability of rolling a number which is a multiple of 5?

____

Name ______________________________

Guided Problem Solving
12-2

Hurricane season in the United States is from June 1 to November 30. In an average season, there are ten tropical storms. Six are expected to reach hurricane strength and two of these are likely to strike the U.S. coast.

Is the probability that a tropical storm will turn into a hurricane more than 50%?

Understand

1. How many tropical storms are there in an average season? ____________
2. How many of the tropical storms are expected to reach hurricane strength in an average season? ____________

Plan

3. Describe the ratio you will use to show the probability that a tropical storm will turn into a hurricane.

____

____

4. What will you compare the ratio to? ____________

Solve

5. Find the probability that a tropical storm will turn into a hurricane. ____________
6. Write the probability as a percent. ________
7. Is the percentage less than, equal to, or greater than 50%? ____________

Look Back

8. How could you answer the question without changing the probability to a percent?

____

____

SOLVE ANOTHER PROBLEM

Suppose 20 tropical storms are predicted.
Twelve are expected to reach hurricane strength.
What percentage will probably *not* become hurricanes? ________

Name ___________________________

Guided Problem Solving
12-3

Hurricanes blow in a spiral around a circular center known as the "eye." If a storm covers a circular area 400 miles wide and its eye is 20 miles wide, what is the probability of an object in a hurricane being in the eye of the hurricane?

Understand

1. What is the width of the hurricane? __________

2. What is the width of the hurricane's eye? __________

3. What shape is the hurricane? The hurricane's eye? __________

Plan

4. Which ratio will you use to find the probability of an object being in the eye of the hurricane? ______

   a. $\frac{\text{Area of the eye}}{\text{Area of the hurricane}}$ b. $\frac{\text{Area of the hurricane}}{\text{Area of the eye}}$

5. Which formula will you use to find the area of the hurricane and of its eye? ______

   a. $A = Bh$ b. $A = s^2$ c. $A = \pi r^2$

Solve

6. What is the area of the hurricane? __________

7. What is the area of the eye of the hurricane? __________

8. What is the probability of an object being in the eye of the hurricane?

   ____

Look Back

9. How can you Solve a Simpler Problem to see if your answer is reasonable?

   ____

   ____

SOLVE ANOTHER PROBLEM

What is the probability of an object being in the eye of a hurricane if the hurricane is 600 miles wide and its eye is 40 miles wide? __________

Name ______________________________

Guided Problem Solving 12-4

The lunch choices of the day are bologna or peanut butter sandwich with either an apple, orange, or banana, and either juice or milk. Draw a tree diagram showing all possible outcomes.

Understand

1. What are you asked to draw? ______________________

2. What will you show on your drawing? ______________________

Plan

3. Which lunch choice will you list

   a. first? ____________ **b.** second? ____________ **c.** third? ____________

Solve

4. Make a tree diagram by listing your first lunch choice and drawing lines to your second and third choices. Then list all possible choices.

Sandwiches **Fruits** **Drinks** **Possible choices**

Look Back

5. How can you check to see if your answer is reasonable?

____

SOLVE ANOTHER PROBLEM

How many possible choices would there be if soda was also available? You can draw a diagram on another sheet of paper to help you. ________

Name ____________________

Guided Problem Solving
12-5

The probability of a newborn child being a girl is about $\frac{1}{2}$. What is the probability of all 5 children in a family being girls?

Understand

1. What is the probability of a newborn child being a girl? ________
2. What are you asked to find?

____

Plan

3. What is the outcome? ______

   a. Gender of the child b. Number of children in family

4. How many possible outcomes are there for each event? ______
5. How many of the possible outcomes normally will be girls? ______
6. How many events are there? ______

Solve

7. Multiply to find the total number of possible outcomes for all events.

   ____ × ____ × ____ × ____ × ____ = ____

8. Multiply to find the number of possible outcomes that result in the birth of a girl for all events.

   ____ × ____ × ____ × ____ × ____ = ____

9. What is the probability of all 5 children in a family being girls as a ratio? ______

Look Back

10. Since the probability given was *about* $\frac{1}{2}$, will your final answer be exact or approximate?

____

SOLVE ANOTHER PROBLEM

What is the probability of all 4 children in a family being boys? ______

Name ______________________

Guided Problem Solving
12-6

Determine if the game is fair. If it is *not*, tell which player has the higher probability of winning.

A nickel and a dime are tossed. The winner is determined as shown.

Tim wins

Vern wins

Maggie wins

Urse wins

Understand

1. How many possible outcomes are there when the coins are tossed? ________

2. How many possible outcomes are the same? ________

Plan

3. What is the probability that Tim will win? ________

4. What is the probability that Maggie will win? ________

5. What is the probability that Vern will win? ________

6. What is the probability that Urse will win? ________

Solve

7. Is the game fair or unfair? Explain.

____

Look Back

8. Both Tim's and Vern's coins show a head and a tail? How do they differ?

____

SOLVE ANOTHER PROBLEM

Suppose Tim, Vern, and Urse toss two nickels. Tim wins if two tails are tossed. Vern wins if two heads are tossed. Urse wins if a head and a tail are tossed. Is the game fair or unfair? Explain.

____

____

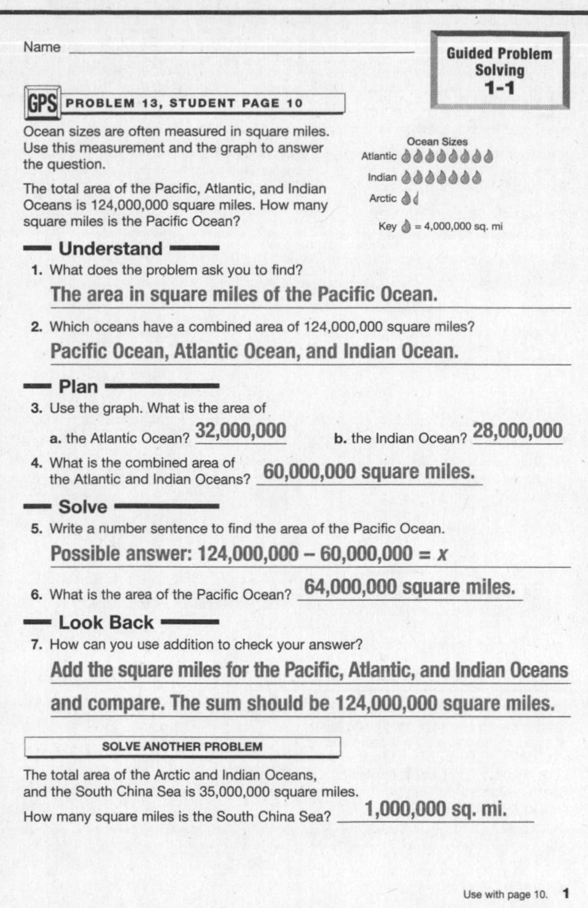

Name ______________________

Guided Problem Solving 1-1

GPS PROBLEM 13, STUDENT PAGE 10

Ocean sizes are often measured in square miles. Use this measurement and the graph to answer the question.

The total area of the Pacific, Atlantic, and Indian Oceans is 124,000,000 square miles. How many square miles is the Pacific Ocean?

Understand

1. What does the problem ask you to find?
   The area in square miles of the Pacific Ocean.
2. Which oceans have a combined area of 124,000,000 square miles?
   Pacific Ocean, Atlantic Ocean, and Indian Ocean.

Plan

3. Use the graph. What is the area of
   a. the Atlantic Ocean? 32,000,000 b. the Indian Ocean? 28,000,000
4. What is the combined area of the Atlantic and Indian Oceans? 60,000,000 square miles.

Solve

5. Write a number sentence to find the area of the Pacific Ocean.
   Possible answer: $124{,}000{,}000 - 60{,}000{,}000 = x$
6. What is the area of the Pacific Ocean? 64,000,000 square miles.

Look Back

7. How can you use addition to check your answer?
   Add the square miles for the Pacific, Atlantic, and Indian Oceans and compare. The sum should be 124,000,000 square miles.

SOLVE ANOTHER PROBLEM

The total area of the Arctic and Indian Oceans, and the South China Sea is 35,000,000 square miles. How many square miles is the South China Sea? 1,000,000 sq. mi.

Use with page 10. 1

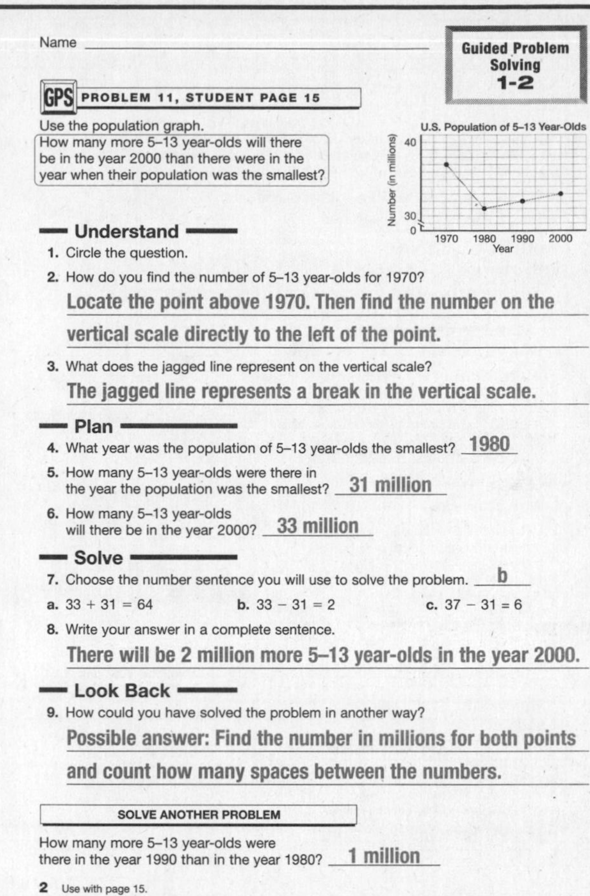

Name ______________________

Guided Problem Solving 1-2

GPS PROBLEM 11, STUDENT PAGE 15

Use the population graph.
How many more 5–13 year-olds will there be in the year 2000 than there were in the year when their population was the smallest?

Understand

1. Circle the question.
2. How do you find the number of 5–13 year-olds for 1970?
   Locate the point above 1970. Then find the number on the vertical scale directly to the left of the point.
3. What does the jagged line represent on the vertical scale?
   The jagged line represents a break in the vertical scale.

Plan

4. What year was the population of 5–13 year-olds the smallest? 1980
5. How many 5–13 year-olds were there in the year the population was the smallest? 31 million
6. How many 5–13 year-olds will there be in the year 2000? 33 million

Solve

7. Choose the number sentence you will use to solve the problem. b
   a. $33 + 31 = 64$ b. $33 - 31 = 2$ c. $37 - 31 = 6$
8. Write your answer in a complete sentence.
   There will be 2 million more 5–13 year-olds in the year 2000.

Look Back

9. How could you have solved the problem in another way?
   Possible answer: Find the number in millions for both points and count how many spaces between the numbers.

SOLVE ANOTHER PROBLEM

How many more 5–13 year-olds were there in the year 1990 than in the year 1980? 1 million

2 Use with page 15.

Name ______________________

Guided Problem Solving 1-3

GPS PROBLEM 11, STUDENT PAGE 20

Use the Calorie Requirements graph. At what age is the difference in calorie needs the greatest between males and females? The smallest? How can you tell?

Calorie Requirements by Age

Key • male ○ female

Number of calories needed: 2000, 3000, 4000

Age (years): 0 10 14 18 22 26 30 34 38 42 46 50 54

Understand

1. What do these points represent?
   a. solid Males' calorie needs.
   b. open Females' calorie needs.
2. What does the distance between two points at any age represent?
   The difference in calorie needs between males and females.

Plan

3. The greatest distance between two points for any age is at age 24.
4. The smallest distance between two points for any age is at age 51.

Solve

5. At what age is the difference in calorie needs the greatest between males and females? How can you tell? 24, because the greatest distance between two points occurs at this age.
6. At what age is the difference in calorie needs the smallest between males and females? How can you tell? 51, because the smallest distance between two points occurs at this age.

Look Back

7. How can you use subtraction to verify your answer? Find the difference in calorie requirements between males and females and then compare differences to find the least and the greatest number.

SOLVE ANOTHER PROBLEM

At what ages is the difference in calorie needs about the same? 18, 30, 34, 38, 42, 46, 50

Use with page 20. 3

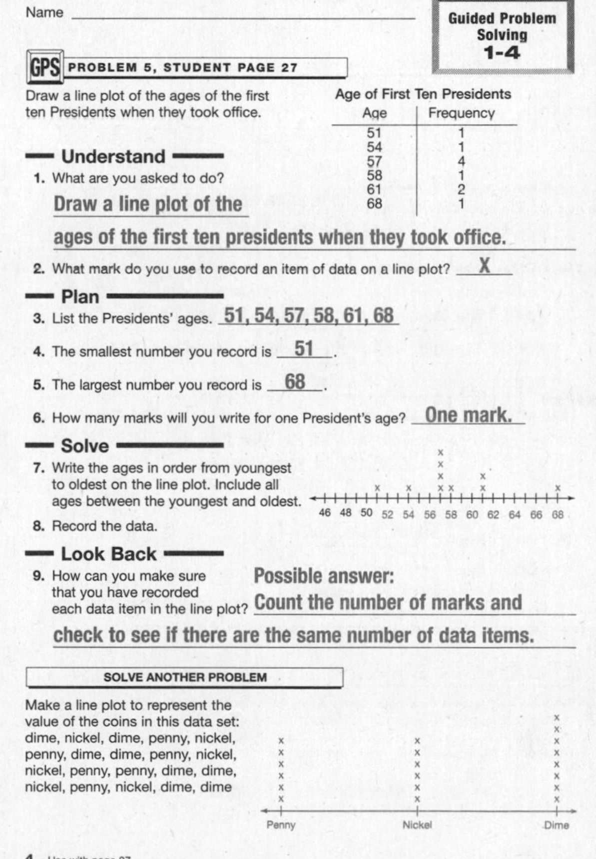

Name ______________________

Guided Problem Solving 1-4

GPS PROBLEM 5, STUDENT PAGE 27

Draw a line plot of the ages of the first ten Presidents when they took office.

Age of First Ten Presidents

Age	Frequency
51	1
54	1
57	4
58	1
61	2
68	1

Understand

1. What are you asked to do?
   Draw a line plot of the ages of the first ten presidents when they took office.
2. What mark do you use to record an item of data on a line plot? X

Plan

3. List the Presidents' ages. 51, 54, 57, 58, 61, 68
4. The smallest number you record is 51.
5. The largest number you record is 68.
6. How many marks will you write for one President's age? One mark.

Solve

7. Write the ages in order from youngest to oldest on the line plot. Include all ages between the youngest and oldest.
8. Record the data.

Look Back

9. How can you make sure that you have recorded each data item in the line plot? Possible answer: Count the number of marks and check to see if there are the same number of data items.

SOLVE ANOTHER PROBLEM

Make a line plot to represent the value of the coins in this data set: dime, nickel, dime, penny, nickel, penny, dime, dime, penny, nickel, nickel, penny, penny, dime, dime, nickel, penny, nickel, dime, dime

4 Use with page 27.

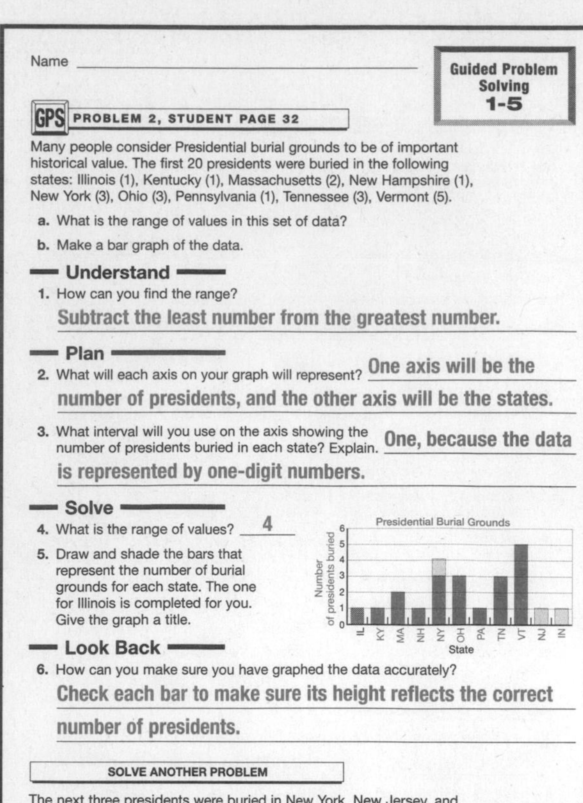

Name ______________________

Guided Problem Solving 1-5

GPS PROBLEM 2, STUDENT PAGE 32

Many people consider Presidential burial grounds to be of important historical value. The first 20 presidents were buried in the following states: Illinois (1), Kentucky (1), Massachusetts (2), New Hampshire (1), New York (3), Ohio (3), Pennsylvania (1), Tennessee (3), Vermont (5).

a. What is the range of values in this set of data?

b. Make a bar graph of the data.

Understand

1. How can you find the range?
   Subtract the least number from the greatest number.

Plan

2. What will each axis on your graph will represent? One axis will be the number of presidents, and the other axis will be the states.
3. What interval will you use on the axis showing the number of presidents buried in each state? Explain. One, because the data is represented by one-digit numbers.

Solve

4. What is the range of values? 4
5. Draw and shade the bars that represent the number of burial grounds for each state. The one for Illinois is completed for you. Give the graph a title.

Look Back

6. How can you make sure you have graphed the data accurately?
   Check each bar to make sure its height reflects the correct number of presidents.

SOLVE ANOTHER PROBLEM

The next three presidents were buried in New York, New Jersey, and Indiana. Use a different color pencil to add this information to your graph. How does this affect the range?

The range remains the same.

Use with page 32. 5

Name ______________________

Guided Problem Solving 1-6

GPS PROBLEM 2, STUDENT PAGE 37

Make a stem-and-leaf diagram from the data.

The ten fastest fish in the world (in miles per hour) include the following: sailfish, 68; blue shark, 43; swordfish, 40; marlin, 50; bluefin tuna, 46; wahoo, 41; tarpon, 35; bonefish, 40; yellowfin tuna, 44; tiger shark, 33.

Understand

1. Underline the speed of each fish.
2. What are you asked to make from the data? c

   a. bar graph **b.** scatterplot **c.** stem-and-leaf diagram

Plan

3. Write the stems from least to greatest. Then write each leaf to the right of its stem as it occurs in the problem.

Stem	Leaf
3	5 3
4	3 0 6 1 0 4
5	0
6	8

Solve

4. Redraw the stem-and-leaf diagram, with the leaves in order from least to greatest.

Stem	Leaf
3	3 5
4	0 0 1 3 4 6
5	0
6	8

Look Back

5. Did you put the tens digits as "stems" and ones digits as "leaves"? Check students' answers.
6. What other ways could you display the data? Possible answer: Bar graph.

SOLVE ANOTHER PROBLEM

Make a stem-and-leaf diagram to organize these data. The average lengths (in feet) of some of the fastest fish in the world are: sailfish, 8; swordfish, 11; marlin, 35; bluefin tuna, 14; wahoo, 3; tarpon, 8; bonefish, 2; yellowfin tuna, 11. Hint: Use zero as one of the stems.

Stem	Leaf
0	8 3 8 2
1	1 4 1
2	
3	5

Stem	Leaf
0	2 3 8 8
1	1 1 4
2	
3	5

6 Use with page 37.

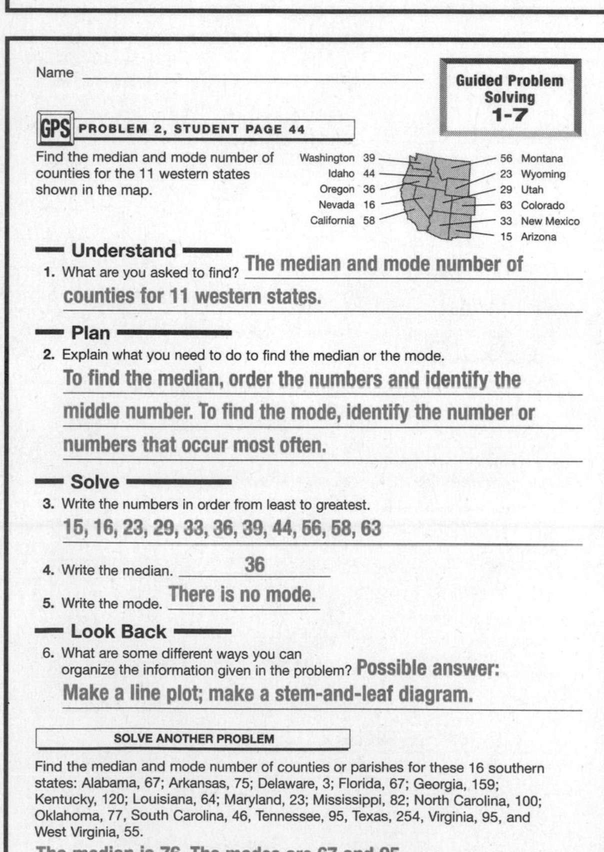

Name ______________________

Guided Problem Solving 1-7

GPS PROBLEM 2, STUDENT PAGE 44

Find the median and mode number of counties for the 11 western states shown in the map.

Understand

1. What are you asked to find? The median and mode number of counties for 11 western states.

Plan

2. Explain what you need to do to find the median or the mode.
   To find the median, order the numbers and identify the middle number. To find the mode, identify the number or numbers that occur most often.

Solve

3. Write the numbers in order from least to greatest.
   15, 16, 23, 29, 33, 36, 39, 44, 56, 58, 63
4. Write the median. 36
5. Write the mode. There is no mode.

Look Back

6. What are some different ways you can organize the information given in the problem? Possible answer: Make a line plot; make a stem-and-leaf diagram.

SOLVE ANOTHER PROBLEM

Find the median and mode number of counties or parishes for these 16 southern states: Alabama, 67; Arkansas, 75; Delaware, 3; Florida, 67; Georgia, 159; Kentucky, 120; Louisiana, 64; Maryland, 23; Mississippi, 82; North Carolina, 100; Oklahoma, 77, South Carolina, 46, Tennessee, 95, Texas, 254, Virginia, 95, and West Virginia, 55.

The median is 76. The modes are 67 and 95.

Use with page 44. 7

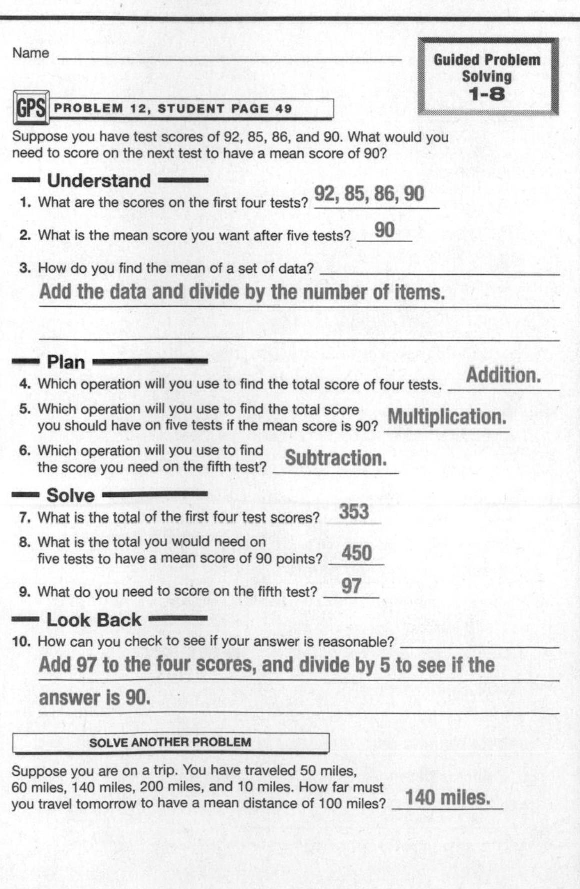

Name ______________________

Guided Problem Solving 1-8

GPS PROBLEM 12, STUDENT PAGE 49

Suppose you have test scores of 92, 85, 86, and 90. What would you need to score on the next test to have a mean score of 90?

Understand

1. What are the scores on the first four tests? 92, 85, 86, 90
2. What is the mean score you want after five tests? 90
3. How do you find the mean of a set of data?
   Add the data and divide by the number of items.

Plan

4. Which operation will you use to find the total score of four tests. Addition.
5. Which operation will you use to find the total score you should have on five tests if the mean score is 90? Multiplication.
6. Which operation will you use to find the score you need on the fifth test? Subtraction.

Solve

7. What is the total of the first four test scores? 353
8. What is the total you would need on five tests to have a mean score of 90 points? 450
9. What do you need to score on the fifth test? 97

Look Back

10. How can you check to see if your answer is reasonable?
    Add 97 to the four scores, and divide by 5 to see if the answer is 90.

SOLVE ANOTHER PROBLEM

Suppose you are on a trip. You have traveled 50 miles, 60 miles, 140 miles, 200 miles, and 10 miles. How far must you travel tomorrow to have a mean distance of 100 miles? 140 miles.

8 Use with page 49.

Name ______________________

Guided Problem Solving 1-9

GPS PROBLEM 9, STUDENT PAGE 53

a. Find the mean, median, and mode with and without the outlier.

b. Did the outlier affect the mode? The mean? The median? Which did it affect the most?

Dinah Shore Tournament Scores (1996)	
Nanci Bowen	285
Susie Redman	286
Brandie Burton	287
Sherri Turner	287
Meg Mallon	292

— Understand —

1. How many times will you need to find the mean, median, and mode for this set of data? **Two times.**

— Plan —

2. Write the data in order from least to greatest. Underline the outlier. **285, 286, 287, 287, 292**

— Solve —

3. Complete the table to find the means, medians, and modes.

	With outlier	Without outlier
Mean	**287.4**	**286.25**
Median	**287**	**286.5**
Mode	**287**	**287**

4. How did the outlier affect the mean, median, and mode? **The mean increased by more than one. The median increased by 0.5. The mode remained the same.**

5. Which did the outlier affect the most? **Mean.**

— Look Back —

6. How can you tell if your answer to Item 4 is reasonable? **Because the outlier was greater than the other data, logically it will increase the mean and median but have little effect on the mode.**

SOLVE ANOTHER PROBLEM

For these scores, calculate the mean, median, and mode, with and without the outlier: 35, 82, 85, 85, 90, 93.

Mean: With, 78.3; Without, 87; Median: With, 85; Without, 85; Mode: With, 85; Without 85.

Use with page 53. 9

Name ______________________

Guided Problem Solving 2-1

GPS PROBLEM 43, STUDENT PAGE 69

For the fact, write the number in word form and in number-word form.

Neptune's mean distance from the sun is 2,798,800,000 miles.

— Understand —

1. How many digits are there in the number? **10 digits.**
2. In which forms will you write the number? **Word and number-word forms.**

— Plan —

3. Write each number of trillions, billions, millions, thousands, and ones.

a. Trillions **0** b. Billions **2** c. Millions **798**

d. Thousands **800** e. Ones **0**

4. Which places have zeros? What is the greatest place value you will use when you write the number in number-word form? **Trillions and ones; billions.**

— Solve —

5. Write the number in number-word form. **2 billion, 798 million, 800 thousand.**
6. Write the entire number in words. **two billion, seven hundred ninety-eight million, eight hundred thousand.**

— Look Back —

7. How can you check your work by reading each number aloud? **Possible answer: The answers to Items 5 and 6 should sound the same when read aloud.**

SOLVE ANOTHER PROBLEM

For the fact, write the number in word form and in number-word form.

Light travels 5,880,000,000,000 miles in one year.

five trillion, eight hundred eighty billion; 5 trillion, 880 billion

10 Use with page 69.

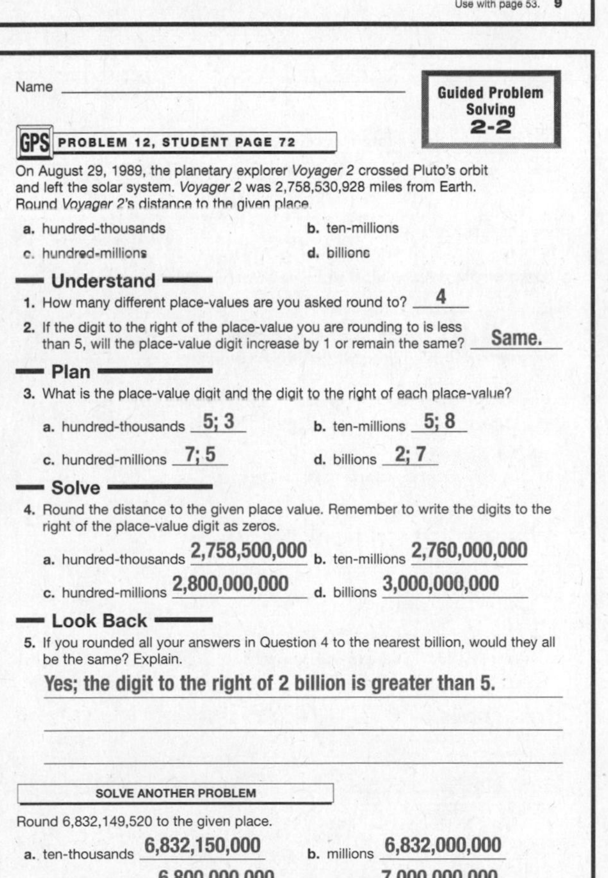

Name ______________________

Guided Problem Solving 2-2

GPS PROBLEM 12, STUDENT PAGE 72

On August 29, 1989, the planetary explorer *Voyager 2* crossed Pluto's orbit and left the solar system. *Voyager 2* was 2,758,530,928 miles from Earth. Round *Voyager 2*'s distance to the given place.

a. hundred-thousands b. ten-millions

c. hundred-millions d. billions

— Understand —

1. How many different place-values are you asked round to? **4**
2. If the digit to the right of the place-value you are rounding to is less than 5, will the place-value digit increase by 1 or remain the same? **Same.**

— Plan —

3. What is the place-value digit and the digit to the right of each place-value?

a. hundred-thousands **5; 3** b. ten-millions **5; 8**

c. hundred-millions **7; 5** d. billions **2; 7**

— Solve —

4. Round the distance to the given place value. Remember to write the digits to the right of the place-value digit as zeros.

a. hundred-thousands **2,758,500,000** b. ten-millions **2,760,000,000**

c. hundred-millions **2,800,000,000** d. billions **3,000,000,000**

— Look Back —

5. If you rounded all your answers in Question 4 to the nearest billion, would they all be the same? Explain. **Yes; the digit to the right of 2 billion is greater than 5.**

SOLVE ANOTHER PROBLEM

Round 6,832,149,520 to the given place.

a. ten-thousands **6,832,150,000** b. millions **6,832,000,000**

c. hundred-millions **6,800,000,000** d. billions **7,000,000,000**

Use with page 72. 11

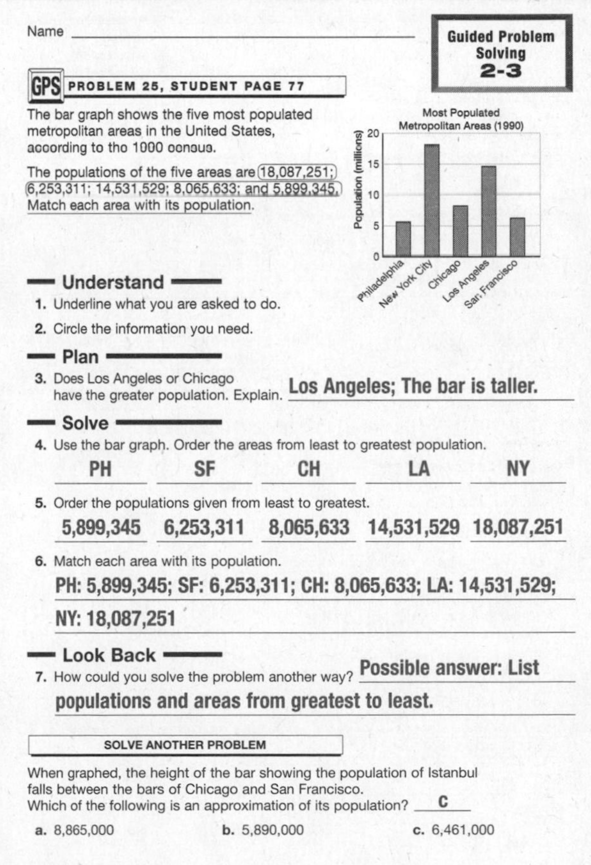

Name ______________________

Guided Problem Solving 2-3

GPS PROBLEM 25, STUDENT PAGE 77

The bar graph shows the five most populated metropolitan areas in the United States, according to the 1990 census.

The populations of the five areas are 18,087,251; 6,253,311; 14,531,529; 8,065,633; and 5,899,345. Match each area with its population.

— Understand —

1. Underline what you are asked to do.
2. Circle the information you need.

— Plan —

3. Does Los Angeles or Chicago have the greater population. Explain. **Los Angeles; The bar is taller.**

— Solve —

4. Use the bar graph. Order the areas from least to greatest population. **PH SF CH LA NY**
5. Order the populations given from least to greatest. **5,899,345 6,253,311 8,065,633 14,531,529 18,087,251**
6. Match each area with its population. **PH: 5,899,345; SF: 6,253,311; CH: 8,065,633; LA: 14,531,529; NY: 18,087,251**

— Look Back —

7. How could you solve the problem another way? **Possible answer: List populations and areas from greatest to least.**

SOLVE ANOTHER PROBLEM

When graphed, the height of the bar showing the population of Istanbul falls between the bars of Chicago and San Francisco. Which of the following is an approximation of its population? **C**

a. 8,865,000 b. 5,890,000 c. 6,461,000

12 Use with page 77.

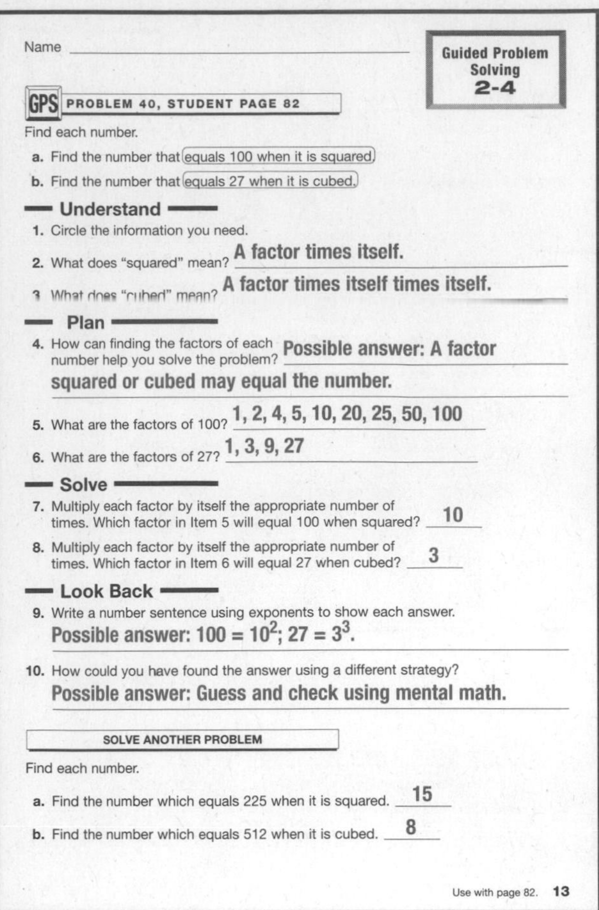

Name ______________________

Guided Problem Solving 2-4

GPS PROBLEM 40, STUDENT PAGE 82

Find each number.

a. Find the number that equals 100 when it is squared.

b. Find the number that equals 27 when it is cubed.

Understand

1. Circle the information you need.
2. What does "squared" mean? **A factor times itself.**
3. What does "cubed" mean? **A factor times itself times itself.**

Plan

4. How can finding the factors of each number help you solve the problem? **Possible answer: A factor squared or cubed may equal the number.**
5. What are the factors of 100? **1, 2, 4, 5, 10, 20, 25, 50, 100**
6. What are the factors of 27? **1, 3, 9, 27**

Solve

7. Multiply each factor by itself the appropriate number of times. Which factor in Item 5 will equal 100 when squared? **10**
8. Multiply each factor by itself the appropriate number of times. Which factor in Item 6 will equal 27 when cubed? **3**

Look Back

9. Write a number sentence using exponents to show each answer. **Possible answer: $100 = 10^2$; $27 = 3^3$.**
10. How could you have found the answer using a different strategy? **Possible answer: Guess and check using mental math.**

SOLVE ANOTHER PROBLEM

Find each number.

a. Find the number which equals 225 when it is squared. **15**

b. Find the number which equals 512 when it is cubed. **8**

Use with page 82. 13

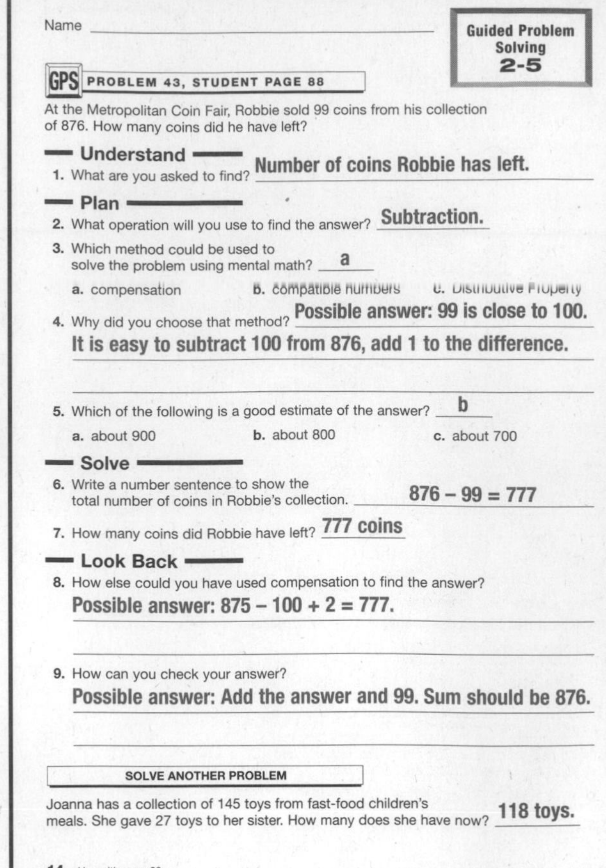

Name ______________________

Guided Problem Solving 2-5

GPS PROBLEM 43, STUDENT PAGE 88

At the Metropolitan Coin Fair, Robbie sold 99 coins from his collection of 876. How many coins did he have left?

Understand

1. What are you asked to find? **Number of coins Robbie has left.**

Plan

2. What operation will you use to find the answer? **Subtraction.**
3. Which method could be used to solve the problem using mental math? **a**

a. compensation b. compatible numbers c. Distributive Property

4. Why did you choose that method? **Possible answer: 99 is close to 100. It is easy to subtract 100 from 876, add 1 to the difference.**
5. Which of the following is a good estimate of the answer? **b**

a. about 900 b. about 800 c. about 700

Solve

6. Write a number sentence to show the total number of coins in Robbie's collection. **876 – 99 = 777**
7. How many coins did Robbie have left? **777 coins**

Look Back

8. How else could you have used compensation to find the answer? **Possible answer: 875 – 100 + 2 = 777.**
9. How can you check your answer? **Possible answer: Add the answer and 99. Sum should be 876.**

SOLVE ANOTHER PROBLEM

Joanna has a collection of 145 toys from fast-food children's meals. She gave 27 toys to her sister. How many does she have now? **118 toys.**

14 Use with page 88.

Name ______________________

Guided Problem Solving 2-6

GPS PROBLEM 23, STUDENT PAGE 92

A picture frame measures 36 in. by 18 in. Estimate the distance around the outside of the frame.

Understand

1. Underline what you are asked to do.
2. What are the dimensions of the frame? **36 in. by 18 in.**

Plan

3. Draw a picture of the rectangular frame. Label the length of each side.

36 in.
18 in. 18 in.
36 in.

4. Which numbers will you add to find the total distance around the frame? **36 + 36 + 18 + 18**
5. Will you use front end-estimation or clustering to estimate the answer. Why? **Possible answer: Front-end, since numbers do not cluster around a convenient number.**

Solve

6. Write a number sentence showing the numbers you used to estimate your answer. **Possible answer: 30 + 30 + 10 + 10 + 30 = 110.**
7. Write a sentence to give the estimated distance around the frame. **Possible answer: The distance around the outside of the picture frame is about 110 inches.**

Look Back

8. How could you find your answer in another way? **Possible answer: Use rounding to estimate.**

SOLVE ANOTHER PROBLEM

A rectangular dog pen measures 96 in. by 84 in. Estimate the distance around the outside of the dog pen. Show the numbers you used to estimate.

Possible answer: 100 + 100 + 80 + 80 = 360; 360 in.

Use with page 92. 15

Name ______________________

Guided Problem Solving 2-7

GPS PROBLEM 35, STUDENT PAGE 96

Flight 777 carries 54 passengers, each with 2 suitcases. Each suitcase weighs, on average, 36 pounds. If the airplane was built to carry 5000 pounds of luggage, is the flight over or under its limit?

Understand

1. What are you asked to find? **Whether the suitcases weigh over or under the weight limit of 5000 pounds.**

Plan

2. Why is it acceptable to estimate to find the answer? **Possible answer: An exact weight of the suitcases is not necessary.**
3. Which method will you use to estimate? **b**

a. Front-end estimation b. Rounding c. Compensation

Solve

4. Estimate the number of suitcases that are on the plane.

2 × **50** = **100**

5. Estimate the total number of pounds that the suitcases weigh.

40 × **100** = **4000**

6. Compare your estimate to 5000 lb. Is the flight over or under its limit? **Under.**

Look Back

7. How could you have solved the problem another way? **Possible answer: Estimate by multiplying any combination of passengers, suitcases, and weights or calculate actual answer.**

SOLVE ANOTHER PROBLEM

Flight 897 carries 48 passengers, each with 2 suitcases. Each suitcase weighs, on average, 43 pounds. If the airplane was built to carry 4800 pounds of luggage, is the flight over or under its limit?

Under; 50 × 2 × 40 = 4000; 4000 < 4800.

16 Use with page 96.

Name ______________________

Guided Problem Solving 2-8

GPS PROBLEM 44, STUDENT PAGE 100

Find an arithmetic expression equal to 9 that contains the following operations.

a. Addition and division
b. Subtraction and division
c. Addition, multiplication, and an exponent

Understand

1. What number must each expression equal? **9**
2. How many expressions will you write? **3 expressions.**

Plan

3. How many operations will you perform in each expression?

a. Part a **2** **b.** Part b **2** **c.** Part c **3**

4. Which operation will you perform first in each expression?

a. Part a **Division.** **b.** Part b **Division.** **c.** Part c **Exponents.**

Solve

Possible answers:

5. To write expression a, choose two numbers and perform the first operation. Show the numbers you choose. **$9 \div 3 = 3$**
6. What number would you need to use with the second operation so that the value of the expression is 9? Write the expression. If you cannot find a number, change the numbers you used in Item 5. **$6 + 9 \div 3$**
7. Repeat the steps in Items 5 and 6 to write expression b. **$10 - 9 \div 9$**
8. To write expression c, repeat the step in Item 5. Choose a number and perform the second operation. Then repeat the steps in Item 7. **$1 + 2 \times 2^2$**

Look Back

9. Find another solution for each problem.

Possible answers: $4 + 25 \div 5$; $15 - 12 \div 2$; $0 + 1 \times 3^2$.

SOLVE ANOTHER PROBLEM

Write an arithmetic expression equal to 12 which contains subtraction, an exponent, and division.

Possible answer: $14 - 2^2 \div 2$.

Name ______________________

Guided Problem Solving 2-9

GPS PROBLEM 34, STUDENT PAGE 106

Jeff is conducting a science experiment with a three-rabbit population. Every month, the rabbit population doubles. How many rabbits will he have after 5 months?

Understand

1. Circle the information you need.
2. What does it mean for the population to "double?" **Two times larger.**
3. Will the rabbit population get larger or smaller? **Larger.**

Plan

4. Will you use addition or multiplication to solve the problem? **Either.**
5. What is the numerical pattern? **Double the preceding number.**
6. Which would be a reasonable answer for the number of rabbits Jeff will have in 5 months? **b**

a. about 20 **b.** about 200 **c.** about 2000

Solve

7. How many rabbits will Jeff have after 1 month? **6 rabbits.**
8. Continue the pattern for months 1, 2, 3, 4, and 5.

3,	**6**,	**12**,	**24**,	**48**,	**96**
after:	1 mo	2 mo	3 mo	4 mo	5 mo

9. Write a sentence to give the final answer.

Possible answer: Jeff will have 96 rabbits after 5 months.

Look Back

10. What other strategies could you have used to find the answer?

Possible answer: Make a Table.

SOLVE ANOTHER PROBLEM

Marie is conducting a science experiment with a four-mouse population. Every 2 months, the mouse population doubles. How many mice will she have after 8 months? **64 mice.**

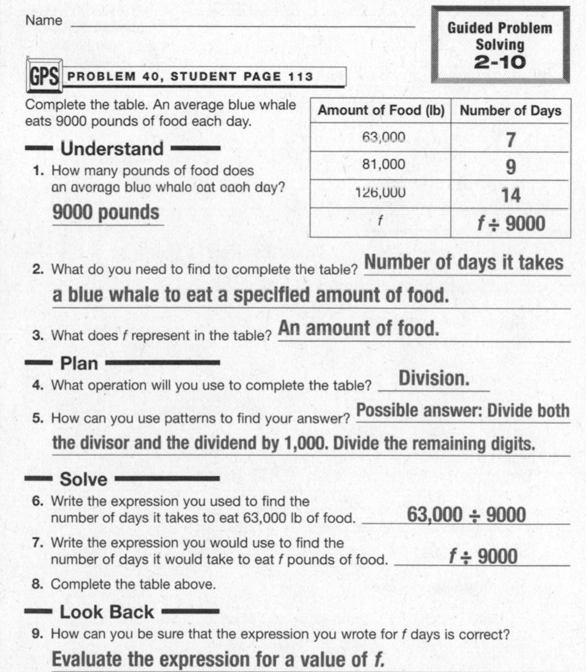

Name ______________________

Guided Problem Solving 2-10

GPS PROBLEM 40, STUDENT PAGE 113

Complete the table. An average blue whale eats 9000 pounds of food each day.

Amount of Food (lb)	Number of Days
63,000	**7**
81,000	**9**
126,000	**14**
f	**$f \div 9000$**

Understand

1. How many pounds of food does an average blue whale eat each day?

9000 pounds

2. What do you need to find to complete the table? **Number of days it takes a blue whale to eat a specified amount of food.**
3. What does f represent in the table? **An amount of food.**

Plan

4. What operation will you use to complete the table? **Division.**
5. How can you use patterns to find your answer? **Possible answer: Divide both the divisor and the dividend by 1,000. Divide the remaining digits.**

Solve

6. Write the expression you used to find the number of days it takes to eat 63,000 lb of food. **$63{,}000 \div 9000$**
7. Write the expression you would use to find the number of days it would take to eat f pounds of food. **$f \div 9000$**
8. Complete the table above.

Look Back

9. How can you be sure that the expression you wrote for f days is correct?

Evaluate the expression for a value of f.

SOLVE ANOTHER PROBLEM

Complete the table. A wild elephant eats 500 pounds of food each day.

Amount of Food (lb)	Number of Days
4,000	**8**
10,500	**21**
x	**$x \div 500$**

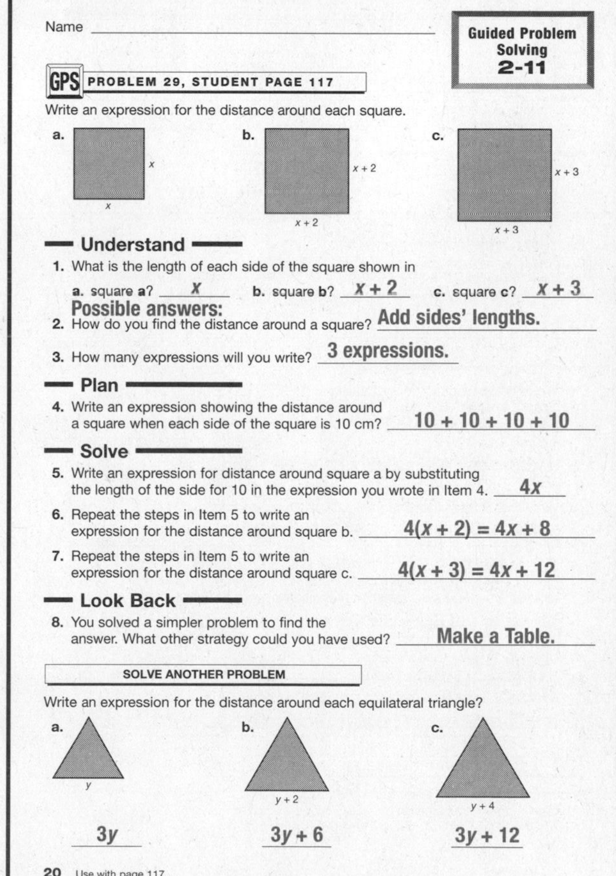

Name ______________________

Guided Problem Solving 2-11

GPS PROBLEM 29, STUDENT PAGE 117

Write an expression for the distance around each square.

a. (square with sides x) **b.** (square with sides $x + 2$) **c.** (square with sides $x + 3$)

Understand

1. What is the length of each side of the square shown in

a. square a? **x** **b.** square b? **$x + 2$** **c.** square c? **$x + 3$**

Possible answers:

2. How do you find the distance around a square? **Add sides' lengths.**
3. How many expressions will you write? **3 expressions.**

Plan

4. Write an expression showing the distance around a square when each side of the square is 10 cm? **$10 + 10 + 10 + 10$**

Solve

5. Write an expression for distance around square a by substituting the length of the side for 10 in the expression you wrote in Item 4. **$4x$**
6. Repeat the steps in Item 5 to write an expression for the distance around square b. **$4(x + 2) = 4x + 8$**
7. Repeat the steps in Item 5 to write an expression for the distance around square c. **$4(x + 3) = 4x + 12$**

Look Back

8. You solved a simpler problem to find the answer. What other strategy could you have used? **Make a Table.**

SOLVE ANOTHER PROBLEM

Write an expression for the distance around each equilateral triangle?

a. (triangle with side y) **b.** (triangle with side $y + 2$) **c.** (triangle with side $y + 4$)

$3y$ **$3y + 6$** **$3y + 12$**

Name ______________________

Guided Problem Solving 2-12

GPS PROBLEM 29, STUDENT PAGE 121

Franz and Jenna built a rectangular treehouse. The north and south walls were each f feet long. The east and west walls were $f + 2$ feet long. The total distance around the treehouse was 24 feet. Was the north wall 6 feet long? Explain.

Understand

1. How do you find the distance around a rectangular figure?
   Add the lengths of the four sides.
2. What is the distance around the treehouse? **24 feet.**
3. What are the dimensions of the treehouse? **f feet by $(f + 2)$ feet**

Plan

4. Write an equation showing the distance around the treehouse.
   Possible answer: $4f + 4 = 24$

Solve

5. Substitute 6 for f in your equation. If the north wall is 6 feet long, what is the distance around the treehouse? **28 feet.**
6. Could the treehouse have a north wall that is 6 feet long? Explain.
   No. If north wall is 6 ft, then adjoining walls must be 8 ft. So distance around is 28 ft. $28 \neq 24$.

Look Back

7. What is another strategy you could use to solve the problem?
   Draw a diagram; label the lengths of the sides and add.

SOLVE ANOTHER PROBLEM

The Hot Shot Club placed a colored border around the outside of the hallway bulletin board. They used 32 feet of crepe paper. The width of the bulletin board was w feet. The length was $w + 4$ feet. Was the width of the bulletin board 6 feet long? Explain.

Yes. Since the distance around is $4w + 8$, substitute 6 for w. $w = 32$, which is the distance given.

Name ______________________

Guided Problem Solving 2-13

GPS PROBLEM 38, STUDENT PAGE 125

Write an equation for the situation and then solve it.

The top three gold-producing countries produce 1171 tonnes (metric tons) of gold. South Africa produces 584 tonnes, Australia produces 256 tonnes. The United States produces u tonnes. How much does the United States produce?

Understand

1. Circle the number of tonnes produced by each country.
2. How many tonnes are produced by the three countries? **1171 tonnes.**

Plan

3. What operation would you use to find the total number of tonnes produced by the three countries? **Addition.**
4. Write an expression showing the number of tonnes produced by the three countries. **$584 + 256 + u$**

Solve

5. Write an equation showing the gold production for the three countries. Use your answer to Item 4 as one side of the equation.
   $584 + 256 + u = 1171$
6. How much gold did South Africa and Australia produce in all? **840 tonnes.**
7. Substitute the total tonnes produced by South Africa and Australia for the two values in your equation. Rewrite the equation.
   $840 + u = 1171$
8. Solve the equation. How much does the United States produce? **331 tonnes.**

Look Back

9. How can you check you answer to be sure it is correct?
   Possible answer: Add answer to tonnes produced by South Africa and Australia to see if the sum is 1171.

SOLVE ANOTHER PROBLEM

Write and solve an equation: One year, Ghana produced 26 tonnes of gold, Mexico produced 9 tonnes, and China produced g tonnes. Together they produced 155 tonnes. How much did China produce?

$26 + 9 + g = 155$; 120 tonnes.

Name ______________________

Guided Problem Solving 3-1

GPS PROBLEM 31, STUDENT PAGE 141

Jarvis made a four-digit number with 0, 3, 6, and 8. The number was smaller than 5 but bigger than 1. What could his number be? Explain.

Understand

1. How many digits will there be in Jarvis's number? **4 digits.**
2. Underline the clue that helps you find the first digit.

Plan

3. Is Jarvis's number a whole number or a decimal? Explain.
   Decimal, because it must have three digits to the right of the decimal point.

Solve

4. Write the first digit of one number made from 0, 3, 6, and 8 in the first box at the right. Explain how you know.

3	.			

   It is the only digit that is between 1 and 5.
5. Write the remaining digits in as many ways as you can.
   3.068, 3.086, 3.608, 3.680, 3.806, 3.860
6. Look at each way you listed the digits in Item 5. Does the order of the remaining three digits make any difference in whether the number is less than 5 or greater than 1? Explain.
   No, all of the decimals are between 1 and 5.

Look Back

7. What strategy can you use to make sure that you have listed all the possible numbers that meet the criteria?
   Possible answer: Make an Organized List.

SOLVE ANOTHER PROBLEM

Agatha made a five-digit number with 0, 3, 5, 8, and 9. The number is bigger than 39 and smaller than 53. The thousandths digit is 3 times the tenths digit. What number did Agatha make? **50.389**

Name ______________________

Guided Problem Solving 3-2

GPS PROBLEM 40, STUDENT PAGE 146

Wendell and Terry both rounded the number 3.4682. Wendell says that he rounded the number up. Terry says that he rounded the number down. To what place value might the number have been rounded by Wendell? By Terry? Explain.

Understand

1. Underline the information that you need.

Plan

2. When is a number rounded up? **When the digit to the right of the place value to be rounded is 5 or greater.**

Solve

3. Would you round each number up or down when rounding to the
   a. ones place? **Down.**
   b. tenths place? **Up.**
   c. hundredths place? **Up.**
   d. thousandths place? **Down.**
4. Wendell rounded up. List all the place values that the number might have been rounded to by Wendell. Explain.
   Tenths or hundredths (3.5 or 3.47); 6 and 8 are greater than 5.
5. Terry rounded down. List all the place values that the number might have been rounded to by Terry. Explain.
   Ones or thousandths (3 or 3.468); 4 and 2 are less than 5.

Look Back

6. Why didn't you check ten-thousandths as a place value?
   Possible answer: There is no digit to its right.

SOLVE ANOTHER PROBLEM

Casey and Jenna both rounded the number 42.185. Casey rounded the number up. Jenna rounded the number down. To what place value might the number have been rounded by Casey? By Jenna? Explain.

Casey: tenths or hundredths (42.2 or 42.19); 8 and 5 are equal to or greater than 5. Jenna: tens or ones (40 or 42); 2 and 1 are less than 5.

Name ______________________

Guided Problem Solving 3-3

GPS PROBLEM 30, STUDENT PAGE 152

The chart shows the finishing times for a swimming race. Who came in first, second, and third?

Swimmer	Time (sec)
Gabe	32.01
Raul	31.84
Josh	31.92

Understand

1. How long did it take Raul to finish the race? **31.84 sec**
2. Is the fastest time less than or greater than the slowest time? Explain. **Less, because the winner takes less time to finish the race.**

Plan

3. To list the times in order, which digits will you compare first? **Tens** Second? **Ones** Third? **Tenths** Fourth? **Hundredths**

Solve

4. Write the times in order from least to greatest. **31.84, 31.92, 32.01**
5. Write the times in order from fastest to slowest. **31.84, 31.92, 32.01**
6. Who came in first? **Raul** Second? **Josh** Third? **Gabe**

Look Back

7. Did you need to compare all the place values to order the times? Explain. **No, order was found after comparing the tenths digits.**

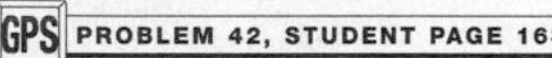

SOLVE ANOTHER PROBLEM

The chart shows the finishing times for a relay race. Who came in first, second, and third?

Raylene, Kenisha, Lynn

Runner	Time (sec)
Lynn	28.10
Kenisha	28.01
Raylene	21.08

Use with page 152. 25

Name ______________________

Guided Problem Solving 3-4

GPS PROBLEM 40, STUDENT PAGE 156

In 1993, the U.S. Post Office released a large number of stamps picturing Elvis Presley. In scientific notation, the exponent is 8. The decimal factor has three digits, all of them odd. It's greater than 5.13, less than 5.19, and all the digits are different. How many Elvis Presley stamps were issued in 1993?

Understand

1. What are you asked to find? **How many Elvis stamps were issued in 1993.**
2. How will the number of stamps be written? **b**
   a. Standard notation b. Scientific notation

Plan

3. Write the power of ten for the number of stamps. **10^8**
4. The digits in the decimal factor are odd. Which digits could be in the decimal factor? **1, 3, 5, 7, 9**
5. The decimal factor is between 5.13 and 5.19. Which digit is
   a. in the ones place? **5** b. in the tenths place? **1**
   c. Since no digit can be repeated in the answer, which digit can be used in the hundredths place? **7**

Solve

6. Combine the information you found in Items 4 and 5 to write a sentence stating how many Elvis stamps were issued in 1993. **There were 5.17×10^8 Elvis stamps issued in 1993.**

Look Back

7. Which strategy did you use to find your answer? **Use Logical Reasoning.**

SOLVE ANOTHER PROBLEM

A number in scientific notation uses only digits that are multiples of 3, except for the base of 10 in the power of ten. Each digit is used once and the number is the largest number possible. What is the number?

6.3×10^9

26 Use with page 156.

Name ______________________

Guided Problem Solving 3-5

GPS PROBLEM 42, STUDENT PAGE 163

You bought four pairs of pants at the same price. Based on rounding, your estimate of the total cost was $40 before tax.

a. If you rounded to the nearest dollar, what is the maximum price for each pair? Explain.

b. If you rounded to the nearest dollar, what is the minimum price? Explain.

Understand

1. Underline the information you need.
2. To estimate, you will round to the nearest **dollar**.

Plan

3. Each pair of pants costs the same amount. What is the estimated cost of each pair of pants? **$10**
4. To find the maximum price, will you look for a number that rounds up or rounds down to 10? Explain. **Rounds down. It is greater than a number rounded up to 10.**

Solve

5. What is the maximum price for each pair of pants? **$10.49**
6. What is the minimum price for each pair of pants? **$9.50**

Look Back

7. Write number sentences to check your answers. **$10.49 + 10.49 + 10.49 + 10.49 = 41.96 \approx 40$; $9.50 + 9.50 + 9.50 + 9.50 = 38 \approx 40$**

SOLVE ANOTHER PROBLEM

You bought three CDs at the same price. Based on rounding, your estimate of the total cost was $36 before tax. If you rounded to the nearest dollar, what is the maximum price for each CD? What is the minimum price? Explain your answers.

Maximum price: $12.49; Minimum price: $11.50; Costs should round to $12 since 36 ÷ 3 = 12.

Use with page 163. 27

Name ______________________

Guided Problem Solving 3-6

GPS PROBLEM 32, STUDENT PAGE 167

One day, 1 Japanese yen was worth 0.0098 U.S. dollars. The same day, a Swedish krona was worth 0.1297 U.S. dollars.

a. How much more was the krona worth than the yen that day?

b. On the same day, 1 Thai baht was worth 0.0398 U.S. dollars. How much U.S. money equals one baht plus one yen?

Understand

1. How many U.S. dollars was one Japanese yen worth? **0.0098**
2. How many U.S. dollars was one Swedish krona worth? **0.1297**
3. How many U.S. dollars was one Thai baht worth? **0.0398**

Plan

4. Which operation will you use to find how much more one currency is than another? **Subtraction.**
5. Which operation will you use to find how much two currencies are worth together? **Addition.**

Solve

6. How much more was the krona worth than the yen? Compare in U.S. dollars. **$0.1199**
7. How many U.S. dollars equal one baht plus one yen? **$0.0496**

Look Back

8. Would a grid model help you find the answer? Explain. **Possible answer: No, it would be difficult to count in a 100×100 grid.**

SOLVE ANOTHER PROBLEM

One day, 1 Canadian dollar was worth 0.7319 U.S. dollars. The same day, a German mark was worth 0.6430 U.S. dollars.

a. How much more was the Canadian dollar worth than the German mark that day? **$0.0889**

b. On the same day, 1 Pakistani rupee was worth 0.0252 U.S. dollars. How much U.S. money equals one mark plus one rupee? **$0.6682**

28 Use with page 167.

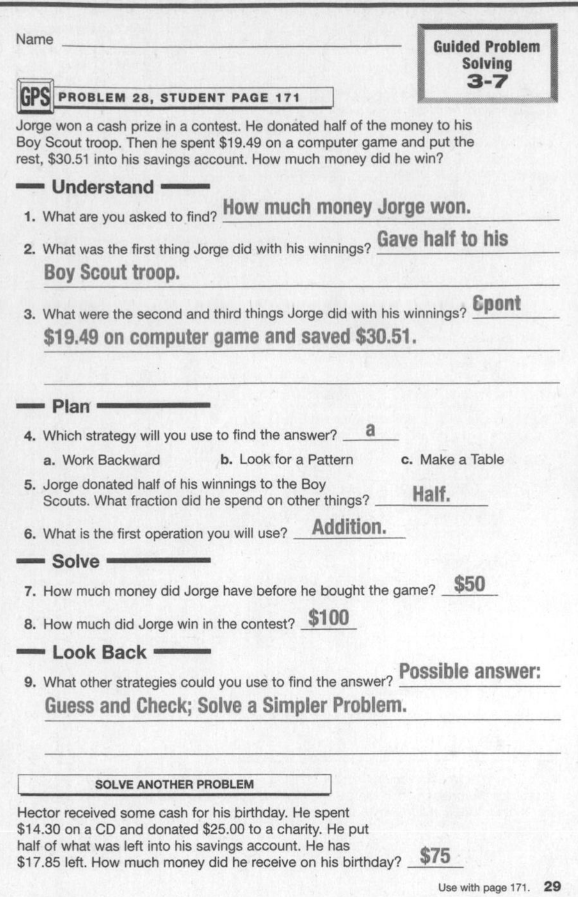

Name ______________________

Guided Problem Solving 3-7

GPS **PROBLEM 28, STUDENT PAGE 171**

Jorge won a cash prize in a contest. He donated half of the money to his Boy Scout troop. Then he spent $19.49 on a computer game and put the rest, $30.51 into his savings account. How much money did he win?

Understand

1. What are you asked to find? **How much money Jorge won.**
2. What was the first thing Jorge did with his winnings? **Gave half to his Boy Scout troop.**
3. What were the second and third things Jorge did with his winnings? **Spent $19.49 on computer game and saved $30.51.**

Plan

4. Which strategy will you use to find the answer? **a**
   a. Work Backward b. Look for a Pattern c. Make a Table
5. Jorge donated half of his winnings to the Boy Scouts. What fraction did he spend on other things? **Half.**
6. What is the first operation you will use? **Addition.**

Solve

7. How much money did Jorge have before he bought the game? **$50**
8. How much did Jorge win in the contest? **$100**

Look Back

9. What other strategies could you use to find the answer? **Possible answer: Guess and Check; Solve a Simpler Problem.**

SOLVE ANOTHER PROBLEM

Hector received some cash for his birthday. He spent $14.30 on a CD and donated $25.00 to a charity. He put half of what was left into his savings account. He has $17.85 left. How much money did he receive on his birthday? **$75**

Name ______________________

Guided Problem Solving 3-8

GPS **PROBLEM 30, STUDENT PAGE 180**

Andrea drinks 54.3 ounces of milk every week. She also drinks a 6-ounce can of orange juice and 8 glasses of water every day. If she drinks 544.3 ounces of liquid in a week and every glass of water is the same size, how big is each glass of water?

Understand

1. What are you asked to find? **How many ounces in one glass.**
2. Circle the data given in ounces per week.
3. Underline the data given in ounces per day.

Plan

4. How will you find how much Andrea drinks in one week when you are given the amount she drinks each day? **Multiply by 7.**
5. How many glasses of water does she drink each day? **8 glasses**
6. How many glasses of water does she drink each week? **56 glasses**
7. How many ounces of orange juice does she drink each week? **42 oz**

Solve

8. How many ounces of milk and juice does she drink each week? **96.3 oz**
9. Subtract to find how many ounces of water she drinks each week. **448 oz**
10. Divide by 56 to find how many ounces each glass of water holds. **8 oz**

Look Back

11. How can you work backward to check your answer? **Multiply 8 oz by 7; multiply 56 by 8; add: 448 + 42 + 54.3 = 544.3; 544.3 oz**

SOLVE ANOTHER PROBLEM

Kelsey earns $65.30 every week working at a grocery store and $5 every day walking a neighbor's dog. She also watches her brother for 2 hours every day. If she earns $128.30 each week, how much does she earn each hour she watches her brother? **$2**

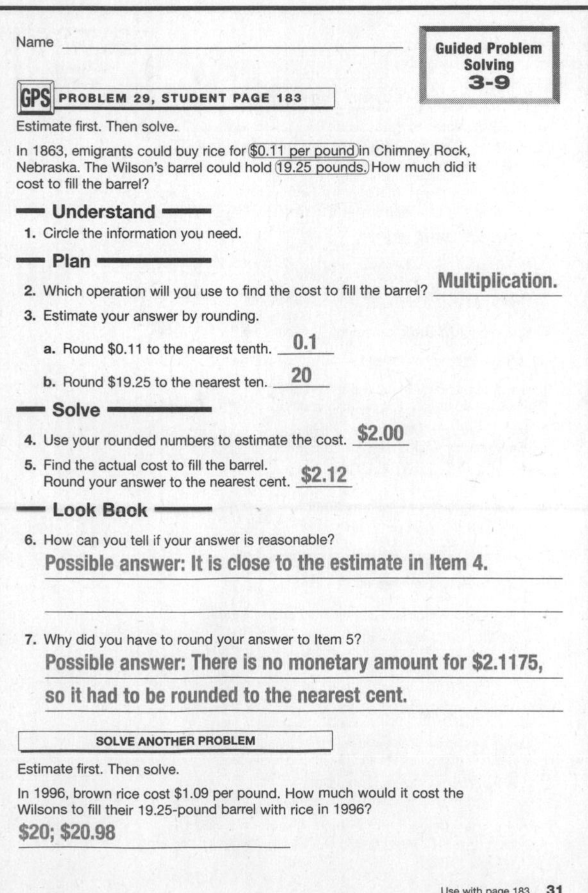

Name ______________________

Guided Problem Solving 3-9

GPS **PROBLEM 29, STUDENT PAGE 183**

Estimate first. Then solve.

In 1863, emigrants could buy rice for $0.11 per pound in Chimney Rock, Nebraska. The Wilson's barrel could hold 19.25 pounds. How much did it cost to fill the barrel?

Understand

1. Circle the information you need.

Plan

2. Which operation will you use to find the cost to fill the barrel? **Multiplication.**
3. Estimate your answer by rounding.
   a. Round $0.11 to the nearest tenth. **0.1**
   b. Round $19.25 to the nearest ten. **20**

Solve

4. Use your rounded numbers to estimate the cost. **$2.00**
5. Find the actual cost to fill the barrel. Round your answer to the nearest cent. **$2.12**

Look Back

6. How can you tell if your answer is reasonable? **Possible answer: It is close to the estimate in Item 4.**
7. Why did you have to round your answer to Item 5? **Possible answer: There is no monetary amount for $2.1175, so it had to be rounded to the nearest cent.**

SOLVE ANOTHER PROBLEM

Estimate first. Then solve.

In 1996, brown rice cost $1.09 per pound. How much would it cost the Wilsons to fill their 19.25-pound barrel with rice in 1996? **$20; $20.98**

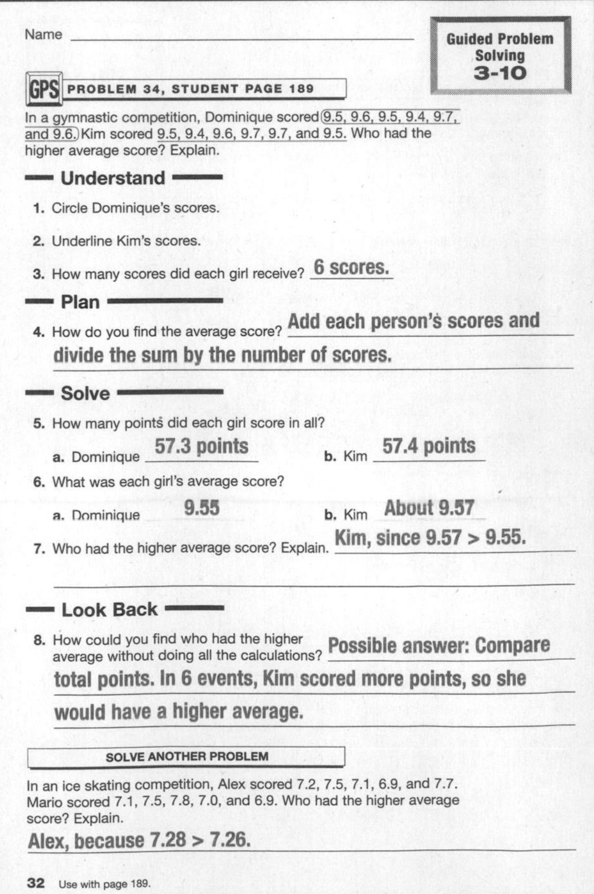

Name ______________________

Guided Problem Solving 3-10

GPS **PROBLEM 34, STUDENT PAGE 189**

In a gymnastic competition, Dominique scored 9.5, 9.6, 9.5, 9.4, 9.7, and 9.6. Kim scored 9.5, 9.4, 9.6, 9.7, 9.7, and 9.5. Who had the higher average score? Explain.

Understand

1. Circle Dominique's scores.
2. Underline Kim's scores.
3. How many scores did each girl receive? **6 scores.**

Plan

4. How do you find the average score? **Add each person's scores and divide the sum by the number of scores.**

Solve

5. How many points did each girl score in all?
   a. Dominique **57.3 points** b. Kim **57.4 points**
6. What was each girl's average score?
   a. Dominique **9.55** b. Kim **About 9.57**
7. Who had the higher average score? Explain. **Kim, since 9.57 > 9.55.**

Look Back

8. How could you find who had the higher average without doing all the calculations? **Possible answer: Compare total points. In 6 events, Kim scored more points, so she would have a higher average.**

SOLVE ANOTHER PROBLEM

In an ice skating competition, Alex scored 7.2, 7.5, 7.1, 6.9, and 7.7. Mario scored 7.1, 7.5, 7.8, 7.0, and 6.9. Who had the higher average score? Explain.

Alex, because 7.28 > 7.26.

Name ______________________

Guided Problem Solving 3-11

GPS PROBLEM 33, STUDENT PAGE 194

Manuel was counting the lights on parade floats. Each float was 36.4 feet long, and they ran bumper to bumper for 5314.4 feet. If there were 150 lights on each float, how many lights did he count?

Understand

1. What are you asked to find? How many lights Manuel counted.
2. Underline the information you need.

Plan

3. How can you find how many floats were in the parade? Divide the total length by the length of a float.
4. Given the number of floats, how can you find the number of lights? Multiply the number of floats by the number of lights on each float.

Solve

5. Write equations showing the number of floats and lights on floats in the parade.

   a. Floats $5314.4 \div 36.4 = 146$ b. Lights $146 \times 150 = 21{,}900$

6. How many lights did Manuel count? 21,900 lights.

Look Back

7. How could you use the strategy, Solve a Simpler Problem, to find the number of lights? Possible answer: Use one-digit whole numbers to discover the steps needed to find the answer.

SOLVE ANOTHER PROBLEM

Cybill was counting the lights on her neighbor's fence. Each section of the fence was 6.2 feet long, and the fence was 210.8 feet long. If there were 25 lights on each section, how many lights did she count?

850 lights.

Name ______________________

Guided Problem Solving 3-12

GPS PROBLEM 31, STUDENT PAGE 198

A wagon weighs 165.3 kg. Carrying riders, the wagon weighs 465 kg. What is the weight of the riders?

Understand

1. How much does the empty wagon weigh? 165.3 kg
2. How much does the wagon with riders weigh? 465 kg

Plan

3. Which operation will you use to find the weight of the riders? Subtraction.
4. Which number sentence would be a good estimate for the weight of the riders? a

   a. $500 - 200 = 300$ b. $500 \times 200 = 1000$ c. $500 + 200 = 700$

Solve

5. How much more does the wagon carrying riders weigh than the empty wagon? 299.7 kg
6. Write a sentence that gives the weight of the riders. Possible answer: The weight of the riders is 299.7 kg.

Look Back

7. Compare the weight you found in Item 5 to your estimate in Item 4. How can you use these two answers to see if your answer is correct? Possible answer: The estimate is 300, and the weight is 299.7. Both amounts are about the same, so the answer is correct.
8. Show another way to check your answer. $299.7 + 165.3 = 465$

SOLVE ANOTHER PROBLEM

A dog weighs 84.8 kg. Carrying a backpack filled with some cans of food, the dog weighs about 100 kg. What is the weight of the cans of food? 15.2 kg

Name ______________________

Guided Problem Solving 4-1

GPS PROBLEM 12, STUDENT PAGE 213

Kristin wants to put organic garbage in a compost pile. She staked out a triangular area on the ground that has two sides of 6 and 8 feet. If the perimeter of the pile is 21 feet, how long is the third side?

Understand

1. What are you asked to find? The length of the third side.
2. What are the lengths of two of the sides? 6 feet and 8 feet.
3. What is the perimeter? 21 feet
4. How do you find the perimeter of a triangle? Add lengths of 3 sides.

Plan

5. Write an addition equation to help you solve the problem. Let s = the length of the side you do not know. $6 + 8 + s = 21$
6. Which of the following is a reasonable range for the length of the third side? b

   a. Less than 5 feet b. Between 5 and 10 feet c. More than 10 feet

Solve

7. Solve the equation. What is the length of the unknown side? 7 feet
8. Write a sentence describing the size and shape of the compost pile. Possible answer: The compost pile is a triangle with sides measuring 6 feet, 7 feet, and 8 feet.

Look Back

9. Write a subtraction equation that you could use to find the length of the third side. Possible answer: $21 - 6 - 8 = s$

SOLVE ANOTHER PROBLEM

Kristin staked out a rectangular area on the ground that has one side measuring 6 feet. If the perimeter of the pile is 28 feet, how long are the other sides?

6 feet, 8 feet, and 8 feet.

Name ______________________

Guided Problem Solving 4-2

GPS PROBLEM 35, STUDENT PAGE 219

Robert and his granddaughter Bailey built a playhouse. The foundation of the playhouse was a 1.86 m-by-95 cm rectangle. What was the perimeter of Bailey's playhouse? Explain.

Understand

1. What are you asked to find? The perimeter of the playhouse.
2. What size and shape is the foundation? 1.86 m by 95 cm; rectangle.
3. How would you find the perimeter of the foundation? Possible answer: Add the lengths of the four sides.

Plan

4. Both dimensions should be in the same unit. What will you do to convert meters to centimeters? Multiply by 100.
5. How many centimeters equal 1.86 meters? 186 centimeters.

Solve

6. Find the perimeter of the foundation in centimeters. 562 centimeters.
7. Explain. How did you find your answer? Convert to one measurement and then add to find the perimeter.

Look Back

8. What is another way you could find the perimeter of the playhouse? Possible answer: Convert cm to m and then find the perimeter.

SOLVE ANOTHER PROBLEM

Allan and Yolanda built a bookcase. The base of the bookcase was a 1.5 m-by-62 cm rectangle. What was the perimeter of their bookcase? Explain.

424 cm or 4.24 m; convert to like units of measure and then find the perimeter.

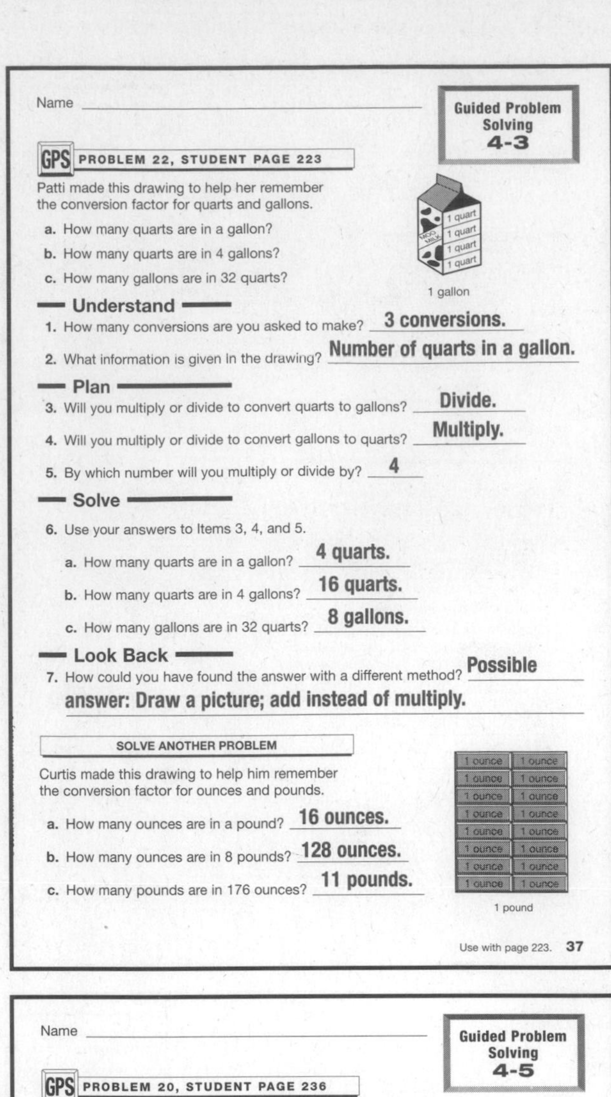

Name ____________________

Guided Problem Solving 4-3

GPS PROBLEM 22, STUDENT PAGE 223

Patti made this drawing to help her remember the conversion factor for quarts and gallons.

a. How many quarts are in a gallon?

b. How many quarts are in 4 gallons?

c. How many gallons are in 32 quarts?

Understand

1. How many conversions are you asked to make? **3 conversions.**
2. What information is given in the drawing? **Number of quarts in a gallon.**

Plan

3. Will you multiply or divide to convert quarts to gallons? **Divide.**
4. Will you multiply or divide to convert gallons to quarts? **Multiply.**
5. By which number will you multiply or divide by? **4**

Solve

6. Use your answers to Items 3, 4, and 5.
   a. How many quarts are in a gallon? **4 quarts.**
   b. How many quarts are in 4 gallons? **16 quarts.**
   c. How many gallons are in 32 quarts? **8 gallons.**

Look Back

7. How could you have found the answer with a different method? **Possible answer: Draw a picture; add instead of multiply.**

SOLVE ANOTHER PROBLEM

Curtis made this drawing to help him remember the conversion factor for ounces and pounds.

a. How many ounces are in a pound? **16 ounces.**

b. How many ounces are in 8 pounds? **128 ounces.**

c. How many pounds are in 176 ounces? **11 pounds.**

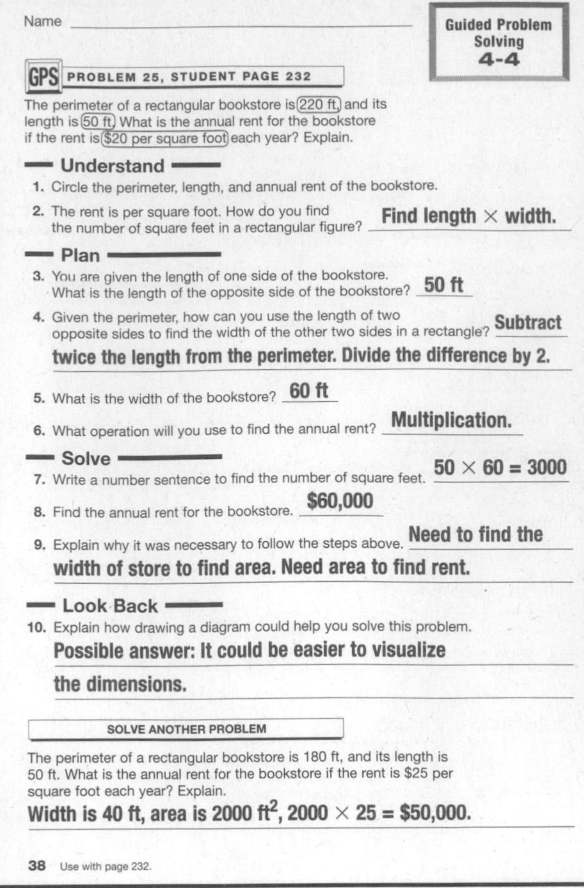

Name ____________________

Guided Problem Solving 4-4

GPS PROBLEM 25, STUDENT PAGE 232

The perimeter of a rectangular bookstore is 220 ft, and its length is 50 ft. What is the annual rent for the bookstore if the rent is $20 per square foot each year? Explain.

Understand

1. Circle the perimeter, length, and annual rent of the bookstore.
2. The rent is per square foot. How do you find the number of square feet in a rectangular figure? **Find length × width.**

Plan

3. You are given the length of one side of the bookstore. What is the length of the opposite side of the bookstore? **50 ft**
4. Given the perimeter, how can you use the length of two opposite sides to find the width of the other two sides in a rectangle? **Subtract twice the length from the perimeter. Divide the difference by 2.**
5. What is the width of the bookstore? **60 ft**
6. What operation will you use to find the annual rent? **Multiplication.**

Solve

7. Write a number sentence to find the number of square feet. **50 × 60 = 3000**
8. Find the annual rent for the bookstore. **$60,000**
9. Explain why it was necessary to follow the steps above. **Need to find the width of store to find area. Need area to find rent.**

Look Back

10. Explain how drawing a diagram could help you solve this problem. **Possible answer: It could be easier to visualize the dimensions.**

SOLVE ANOTHER PROBLEM

The perimeter of a rectangular bookstore is 180 ft, and its length is 50 ft. What is the annual rent for the bookstore if the rent is $25 per square foot each year? Explain.

Width is 40 ft, area is 2000 ft^2, 2000 × 25 = $50,000.

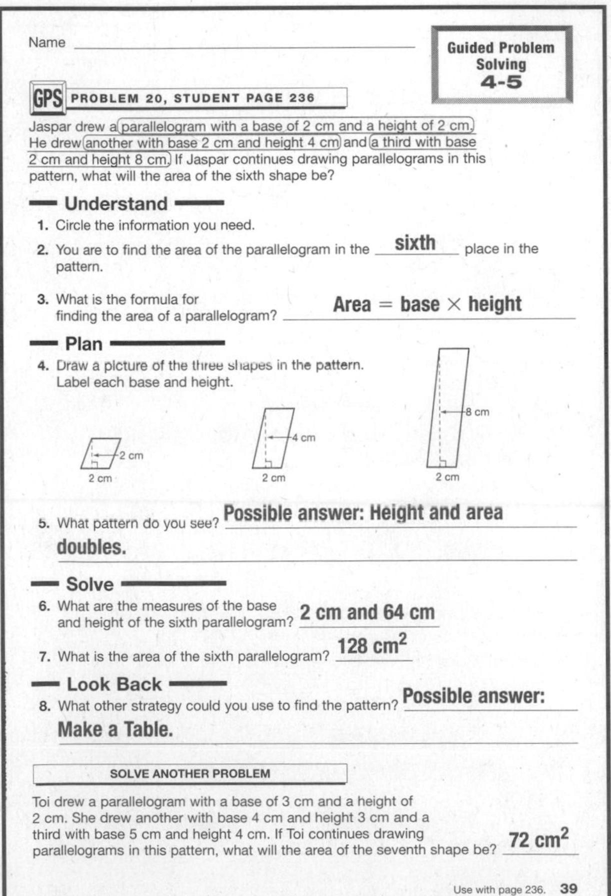

Name ____________________

Guided Problem Solving 4-5

GPS PROBLEM 20, STUDENT PAGE 236

Jaspar drew a parallelogram with a base of 2 cm and a height of 2 cm. He drew another with base 2 cm and height 4 cm and a third with base 2 cm and height 8 cm. If Jaspar continues drawing parallelograms in this pattern, what will the area of the sixth shape be?

Understand

1. Circle the information you need.
2. You are to find the area of the parallelogram in the **sixth** place in the pattern.
3. What is the formula for finding the area of a parallelogram? **Area = base × height**

Plan

4. Draw a picture of the three shapes in the pattern. Label each base and height.

5. What pattern do you see? **Possible answer: Height and area doubles.**

Solve

6. What are the measures of the base and height of the sixth parallelogram? **2 cm and 64 cm**
7. What is the area of the sixth parallelogram? **128 cm^2**

Look Back

8. What other strategy could you use to find the pattern? **Possible answer: Make a Table.**

SOLVE ANOTHER PROBLEM

Toi drew a parallelogram with a base of 3 cm and a height of 2 cm. She drew another with base 4 cm and height 3 cm and a third with base 5 cm and height 4 cm. If Toi continues drawing parallelograms in this pattern, what will the area of the seventh shape be? **72 cm^2**

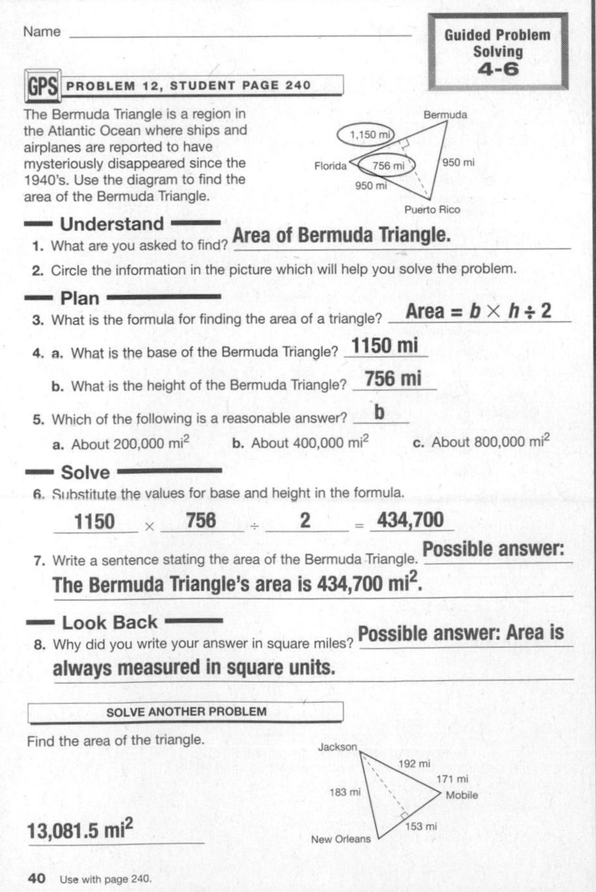

Name ____________________

Guided Problem Solving 4-6

GPS PROBLEM 12, STUDENT PAGE 240

The Bermuda Triangle is a region in the Atlantic Ocean where ships and airplanes are reported to have mysteriously disappeared since the 1940's. Use the diagram to find the area of the Bermuda Triangle.

Understand

1. What are you asked to find? **Area of Bermuda Triangle.**
2. Circle the information in the picture which will help you solve the problem.

Plan

3. What is the formula for finding the area of a triangle? **Area = $b \times h \div 2$**
4. a. What is the base of the Bermuda Triangle? **1150 mi**
   b. What is the height of the Bermuda Triangle? **756 mi**
5. Which of the following is a reasonable answer? **b**
   a. About 200,000 mi^2 b. About 400,000 mi^2 c. About 800,000 mi^2

Solve

6. Substitute the values for base and height in the formula.
   1150 × **756** ÷ **2** = **434,700**
7. Write a sentence stating the area of the Bermuda Triangle. **Possible answer: The Bermuda Triangle's area is 434,700 mi^2.**

Look Back

8. Why did you write your answer in square miles? **Possible answer: Area is always measured in square units.**

SOLVE ANOTHER PROBLEM

Find the area of the triangle.

13,081.5 mi^2

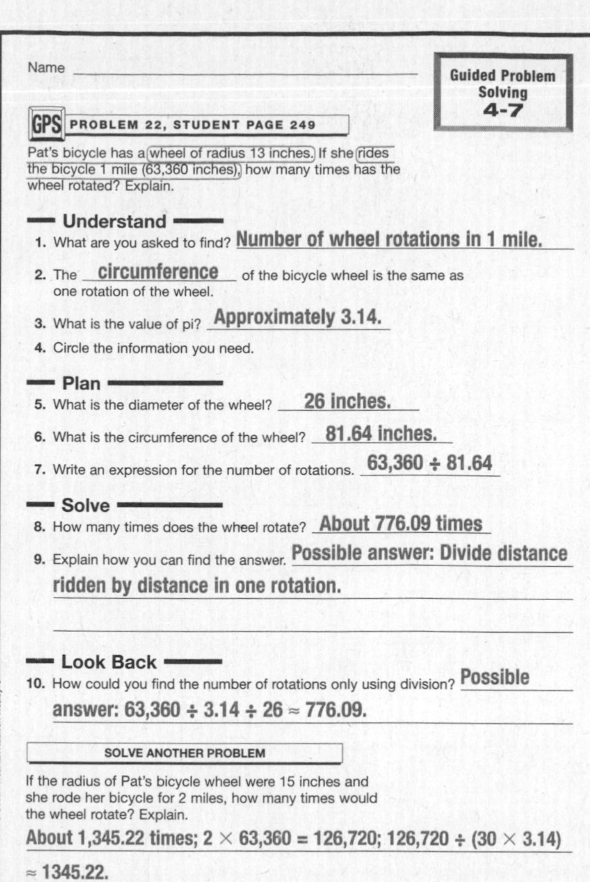

Name ______________________

Guided Problem Solving 4-7

GPS PROBLEM 22, STUDENT PAGE 249

Pat's bicycle has a wheel of radius 13 inches. If she rides the bicycle 1 mile (63,360 inches), how many times has the wheel rotated? Explain.

— Understand —

1. What are you asked to find? **Number of wheel rotations in 1 mile.**
2. The **circumference** of the bicycle wheel is the same as one rotation of the wheel.
3. What is the value of pi? **Approximately 3.14.**
4. Circle the information you need.

— Plan —

5. What is the diameter of the wheel? **26 inches.**
6. What is the circumference of the wheel? **81.64 inches.**
7. Write an expression for the number of rotations. **63,360 ÷ 81.64**

— Solve —

8. How many times does the wheel rotate? **About 776.09 times**
9. Explain how you can find the answer. **Possible answer: Divide distance ridden by distance in one rotation.**

— Look Back —

10. How could you find the number of rotations only using division? **Possible answer: 63,360 ÷ 3.14 ÷ 26 ≈ 776.09.**

SOLVE ANOTHER PROBLEM

If the radius of Pat's bicycle wheel were 15 inches and she rode her bicycle for 2 miles, how many times would the wheel rotate? Explain.

About 1,345.22 times; $2 \times 63,360 = 126,720$; $126,720 \div (30 \times 3.14) \approx 1345.22$.

Use with page 249. 41

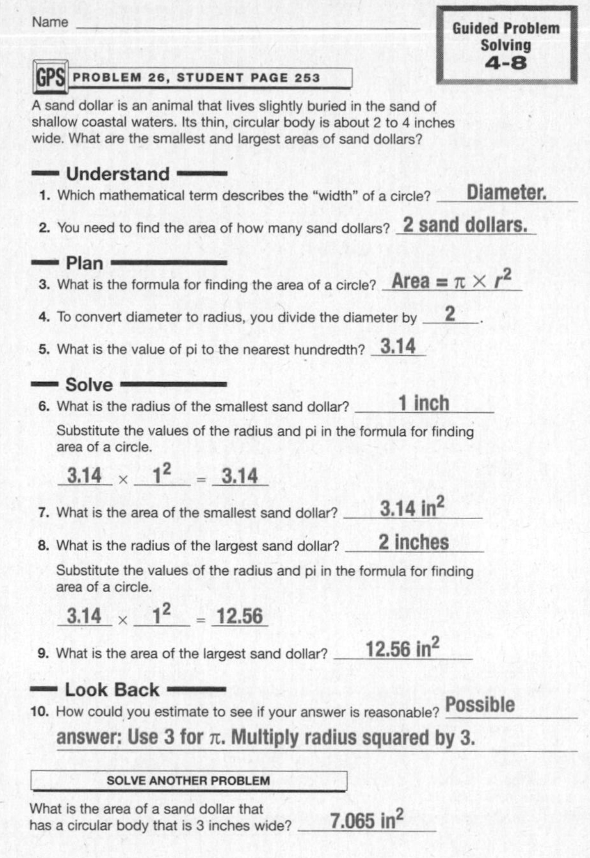

Name ______________________

Guided Problem Solving 4-8

GPS PROBLEM 26, STUDENT PAGE 253

A sand dollar is an animal that lives slightly buried in the sand of shallow coastal waters. Its thin, circular body is about 2 to 4 inches wide. What are the smallest and largest areas of sand dollars?

— Understand —

1. Which mathematical term describes the "width" of a circle? **Diameter.**
2. You need to find the area of how many sand dollars? **2 sand dollars.**

— Plan —

3. What is the formula for finding the area of a circle? **$\text{Area} = \pi \times r^2$**
4. To convert diameter to radius, you divide the diameter by **2**.
5. What is the value of pi to the nearest hundredth? **3.14**

— Solve —

6. What is the radius of the smallest sand dollar? **1 inch**

   Substitute the values of the radius and pi in the formula for finding area of a circle.

   $3.14 \times 1^2 = 3.14$
7. What is the area of the smallest sand dollar? **3.14 in^2**
8. What is the radius of the largest sand dollar? **2 inches**

   Substitute the values of the radius and pi in the formula for finding area of a circle.

   $3.14 \times 1^2 = 12.56$
9. What is the area of the largest sand dollar? **12.56 in^2**

— Look Back —

10. How could you estimate to see if your answer is reasonable? **Possible answer: Use 3 for π. Multiply radius squared by 3.**

SOLVE ANOTHER PROBLEM

What is the area of a sand dollar that has a circular body that is 3 inches wide? **7.065 in^2**

42 Use with page 253.

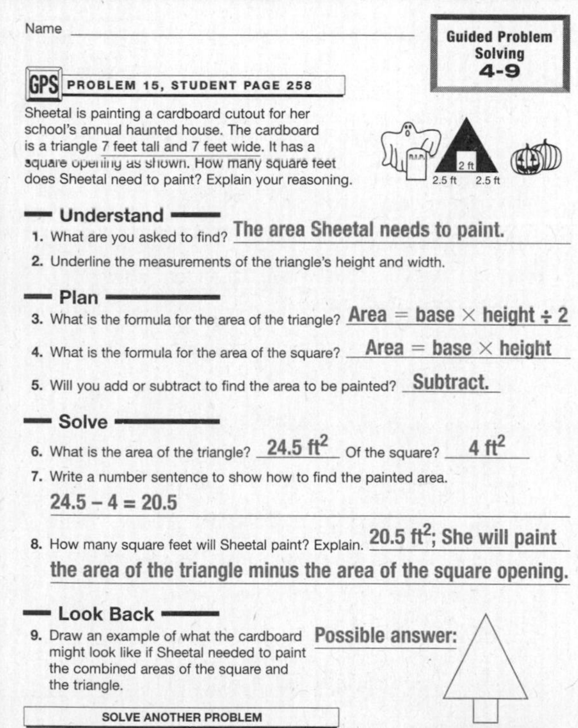

Name ______________________

Guided Problem Solving 4-9

GPS PROBLEM 15, STUDENT PAGE 258

Sheetal is painting a cardboard cutout for her school's annual haunted house. The cardboard is a triangle 7 feet tall and 7 feet wide. It has a square opening as shown. How many square feet does Sheetal need to paint? Explain your reasoning.

— Understand —

1. What are you asked to find? **The area Sheetal needs to paint.**
2. Underline the measurements of the triangle's height and width.

— Plan —

3. What is the formula for the area of the triangle? **Area = base × height ÷ 2**
4. What is the formula for the area of the square? **Area = base × height**
5. Will you add or subtract to find the area to be painted? **Subtract.**

— Solve —

6. What is the area of the triangle? **24.5 ft^2** Of the square? **4 ft^2**
7. Write a number sentence to show how to find the painted area.

   $24.5 - 4 = 20.5$
8. How many square feet will Sheetal paint? Explain. **20.5 ft^2; She will paint the area of the triangle minus the area of the square opening.**

— Look Back —

9. Draw an example of what the cardboard might look like if Sheetal needed to paint the combined areas of the square and the triangle. **Possible answer:**

SOLVE ANOTHER PROBLEM

Liam is painting a cardboard cutout. The cardboard is a square with 8-ft sides, and it has a circular opening as shown. About how many square feet does Liam need to paint? Explain your reasoning.

About 35.74 ft^2; $8 \times 8 - (3.14 \times 3^2) = 35.74$

Use with page 258. 43

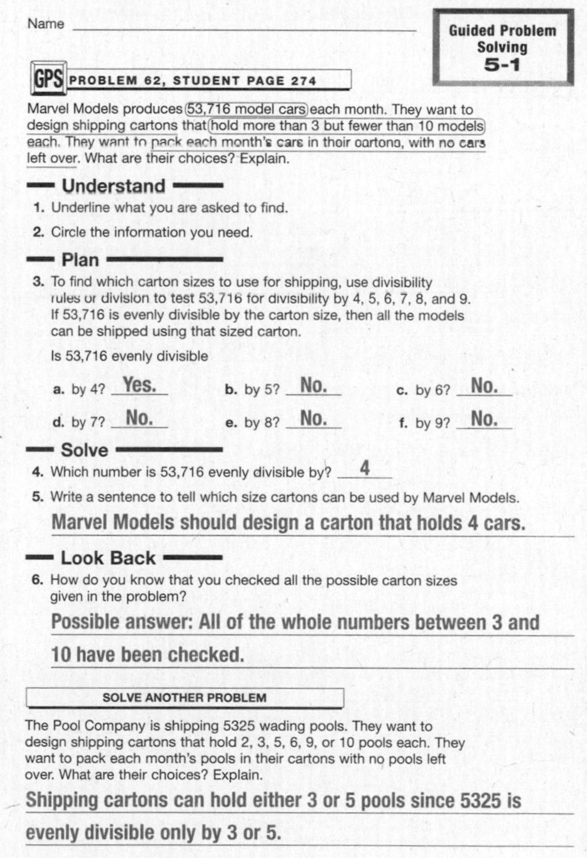

Name ______________________

Guided Problem Solving 5-1

GPS PROBLEM 62, STUDENT PAGE 274

Marvel Models produces 53,716 model cars each month. They want to design shipping cartons that hold more than 3 but fewer than 10 models each. They want to pack each month's cars in their cartons, with no cars left over. What are their choices? Explain.

— Understand —

1. Underline what you are asked to find.
2. Circle the information you need.

— Plan —

3. To find which carton sizes to use for shipping, use divisibility rules or division to test 53,716 for divisibility by 4, 5, 6, 7, 8, and 9. If 53,716 is evenly divisible by the carton size, then all the models can be shipped using that sized carton.

   Is 53,716 evenly divisible

   a. by 4? **Yes.** b. by 5? **No.** c. by 6? **No.**

   d. by 7? **No.** e. by 8? **No.** f. by 9? **No.**

— Solve —

4. Which number is 53,716 evenly divisible by? **4**
5. Write a sentence to tell which size cartons can be used by Marvel Models.

   Marvel Models should design a carton that holds 4 cars.

— Look Back —

6. How do you know that you checked all the possible carton sizes given in the problem?

   Possible answer: All of the whole numbers between 3 and 10 have been checked.

SOLVE ANOTHER PROBLEM

The Pool Company is shipping 5325 wading pools. They want to design shipping cartons that hold 2, 3, 5, 6, 9, or 10 pools each. They want to pack each month's pools in their cartons with no pools left over. What are their choices? Explain.

Shipping cartons can hold either 3 or 5 pools since 5325 is evenly divisible only by 3 or 5.

44 Use with page 274.

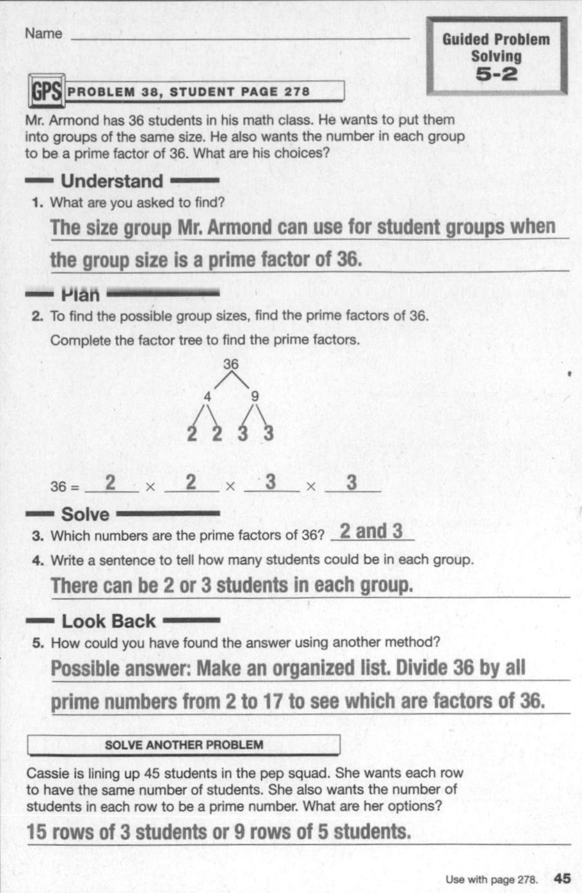

Name ______________________

Guided Problem Solving 5-2

GPS **PROBLEM 38, STUDENT PAGE 278**

Mr. Armond has 36 students in his math class. He wants to put them into groups of the same size. He also wants the number in each group to be a prime factor of 36. What are his choices?

Understand

1. What are you asked to find?
   The size group Mr. Armond can use for student groups when the group size is a prime factor of 36.

Plan

2. To find the possible group sizes, find the prime factors of 36.
   Complete the factor tree to find the prime factors.

   36 → 4, 9; 4 → 2, 2; 9 → 3, 3

   36 = 2 × 2 × 3 × 3

Solve

3. Which numbers are the prime factors of 36? 2 and 3
4. Write a sentence to tell how many students could be in each group.
   There can be 2 or 3 students in each group.

Look Back

5. How could you have found the answer using another method?
   Possible answer: Make an organized list. Divide 36 by all prime numbers from 2 to 17 to see which are factors of 36.

SOLVE ANOTHER PROBLEM

Cassie is lining up 45 students in the pep squad. She wants each row to have the same number of students. She also wants the number of students in each row to be a prime number. What are her options?

15 rows of 3 students or 9 rows of 5 students.

Name ______________________

Guided Problem Solving 5-3

GPS **PROBLEM 41, STUDENT PAGE 284**

In a middle school, the principal plans to hide prizes in the new lockers for the students. The principal plans to put a binder in every 10th locker, a school tee shirt in every in every 15th locker, and a new backpack in every 50th locker. If she starts counting at locker number 1, what is the number of the first locker in which the principal will put all three prizes?

Understand

1. Restate the problem in your own words. Possible answer:
   Every 10th locker has a binder, every 15th locker has a tee shirt, and every 50th locker has a backpack. Find the first locker that will have all three prizes.
2. Underline the information you need.

Plan

3. Find the least common multiple for 10, 15, and 50.
   a. List multiples of 10:
      10, 20, 30, 40, 50, 60, 70, 80, 90, 100, 110, 120, 130, 140, 150
   b. List multiples of 15: 15, 30, 45, 60, 75, 90, 105, 120, 135, 150
   c. List multiples of 50: 50, 100, 150, 200

Solve

4. What is the least common multiple of 10, 15, and 50? 150
5. Which will be the first locker to contain a binder, a tee shirt, and a backpack? The 150th locker.

Look Back

6. What is another way you could solve the problem?
   Use this strategy: Draw a Diagram.

SOLVE ANOTHER PROBLEM

Ernesto, Michelina, and Kale volunteer at the zoo. Ernesto works every 5 days. Michelina works every 6 days. Kale works every 15 days. They work together today. How many days will it be until the next time they work together? 30 days.

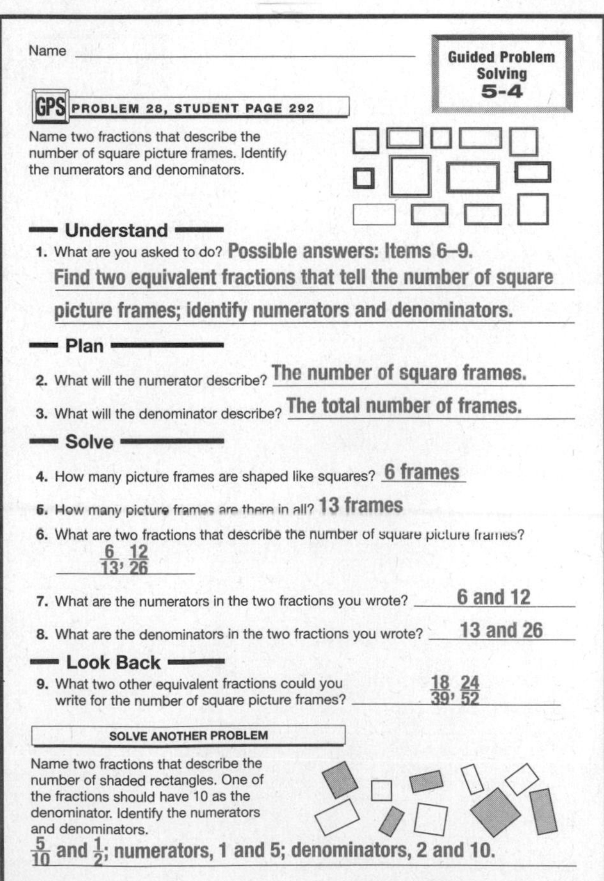

Name ______________________

Guided Problem Solving 5-4

GPS **PROBLEM 28, STUDENT PAGE 292**

Name two fractions that describe the number of square picture frames. Identify the numerators and denominators.

Understand

1. What are you asked to do? Possible answers: Items 6–9.
   Find two equivalent fractions that tell the number of square picture frames; identify numerators and denominators.

Plan

2. What will the numerator describe? The number of square frames.
3. What will the denominator describe? The total number of frames.

Solve

4. How many picture frames are shaped like squares? 6 frames
5. How many picture frames are there in all? 13 frames
6. What are two fractions that describe the number of square picture frames?
   $\frac{6}{13}, \frac{12}{26}$
7. What are the numerators in the two fractions you wrote? 6 and 12
8. What are the denominators in the two fractions you wrote? 13 and 26

Look Back

9. What two other equivalent fractions could you write for the number of square picture frames? $\frac{18}{39}, \frac{24}{52}$

SOLVE ANOTHER PROBLEM

Name two fractions that describe the number of shaded rectangles. One of the fractions should have 10 as the denominator. Identify the numerators and denominators.

$\frac{5}{10}$ and $\frac{1}{2}$; numerators, 1 and 5; denominators, 2 and 10.

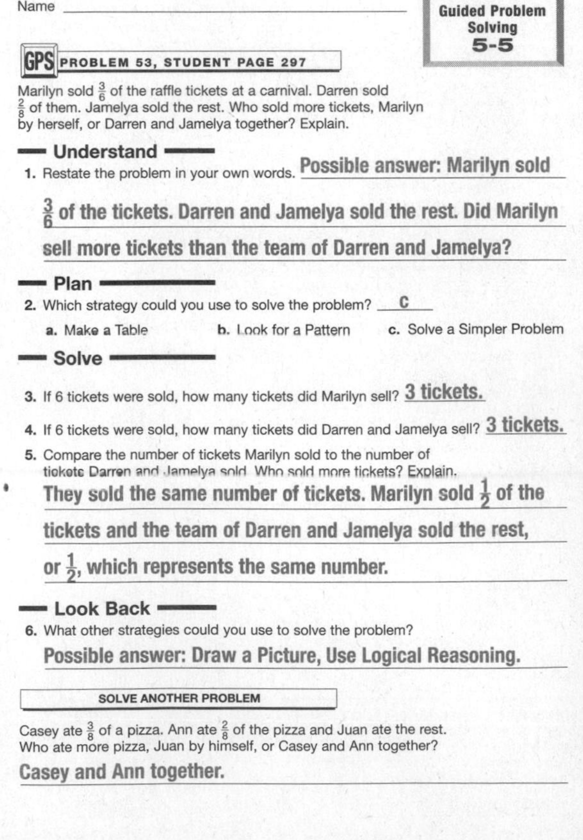

Name ______________________

Guided Problem Solving 5-5

GPS **PROBLEM 53, STUDENT PAGE 297**

Marilyn sold $\frac{3}{6}$ of the raffle tickets at a carnival. Darren sold $\frac{2}{8}$ of them. Jamelya sold the rest. Who sold more tickets, Marilyn by herself, or Darren and Jamelya together? Explain.

Understand

1. Restate the problem in your own words. Possible answer: Marilyn sold $\frac{3}{6}$ of the tickets. Darren and Jamelya sold the rest. Did Marilyn sell more tickets than the team of Darren and Jamelya?

Plan

2. Which strategy could you use to solve the problem? c
   a. Make a Table b. Look for a Pattern c. Solve a Simpler Problem

Solve

3. If 6 tickets were sold, how many tickets did Marilyn sell? 3 tickets.
4. If 6 tickets were sold, how many tickets did Darren and Jamelya sell? 3 tickets.
5. Compare the number of tickets Marilyn sold to the number of tickets Darren and Jamelya sold. Who sold more tickets? Explain.
   They sold the same number of tickets. Marilyn sold $\frac{1}{2}$ of the tickets and the team of Darren and Jamelya sold the rest, or $\frac{1}{2}$, which represents the same number.

Look Back

6. What other strategies could you use to solve the problem?
   Possible answer: Draw a Picture, Use Logical Reasoning.

SOLVE ANOTHER PROBLEM

Casey ate $\frac{3}{8}$ of a pizza. Ann ate $\frac{2}{8}$ of the pizza and Juan ate the rest. Who ate more pizza, Juan by himself, or Casey and Ann together?

Casey and Ann together.

Name ____________

Guided Problem Solving 5-6

GPS PROBLEM 29, STUDENT PAGE 300

Caesar has a tool box that is $15\frac{3}{4}$ in. long. His hammer is $\frac{45}{4}$ in. long. Will the hammer fit in the tool box?

Understand

1. What do you need to find?

   Whether or not the hammer will fit in the tool box.

2. Circle the information you need.

Plan

3. For the hammer to fit in the tool box, should the length of the hammer be longer or shorter than the length of the tool box? Shorter than.

4. Write $\frac{45}{4}$ as a mixed number. $11\frac{1}{4}$

5. Compare the whole number of the number you wrote in Item 4 with the whole number in $15\frac{3}{4}$. Which is greater? 15

Solve

6. Will the hammer fit in the tool box? Explain how you know.

   The hammer will fit in the tool box since $15\frac{3}{4}$ in. is longer than $11\frac{1}{4}$ in. This assumes that the width of the hammer is also less than the width of the tool box.

Look Back

7. Can you think of another way to solve the problem? Explain.

   Possible answer: Convert the tool box length to an improper fraction and then compare the numerators.

SOLVE ANOTHER PROBLEM

Yoko has $2\frac{5}{8}$ pounds of trail mix in one bag. Sam has $\frac{10}{8}$ pounds of trail mix in ten bags. Who has more trail mix? Explain how you know.

Yoko has more trail mix since $2\frac{5}{8}$ is more than $1\frac{2}{8}$.

Name ____________

Guided Problem Solving 5-7

GPS PROBLEM 43, STUDENT PAGE 305

Melissa is using a set of wrenches that come in these sizes: 0.125 inch, 0.25 inch, 0.375 inch, 0.5 inch, 0.625 inch, 0.75 inch, and 0.875 inch. Write each wrench size as a fraction in lowest terms.

Understand

1. What are you asked to find?

   The size of each wrench as a fraction in lowest terms.

Plan

2. Write the steps to follow when you write a decimal as a fraction.

   Write the digits in a decimal as the numerator. Use the place value of the decimal as the denominator.

3. Use your rule to write 0.125 as a fraction. $\frac{125}{1000}$

4. Find the greatest common factor for the numerator and denominator. 125

Solve

5. Use the greatest common factor to write the fraction in lowest terms. $\frac{1}{8}$

6. Repeat steps 3 through 5 for the remaining decimals.

   a. 0.25 $\frac{1}{4}$ b. 0.375 $\frac{3}{8}$ c. 0.5 $\frac{1}{2}$

   d. 0.625 $\frac{5}{8}$ e. 0.75 $\frac{3}{4}$ f. 0.875 $\frac{7}{8}$

Look Back

7. Check your answers by converting the fractions to decimals. Are the decimals you find the same as the original decimals?

   $\frac{1}{8} = 0.125$, $\frac{1}{4} = 0.25$, $\frac{3}{8} = 0.375$, $\frac{1}{2} = 0.5$, $\frac{5}{8} = 0.625$, $\frac{3}{4} = 0.75$, $\frac{7}{8} = 0.875$ Yes, they are the same.

SOLVE ANOTHER PROBLEM

Timothy bought some salads for a party. The salads weighed 0.6 pound, 0.25 pound, 0.15 pound, and 0.375 pound. Write each weight as a fraction in lowest terms.

0.6 lb = $\frac{3}{5}$ lb, 0.25 lb = $\frac{1}{4}$ lb, 0.15 lb = $\frac{3}{20}$ lb, 0.375 lb = $\frac{3}{8}$ lb

Name ____________

Guided Problem Solving 5-8

GPS PROBLEM 28, STUDENT PAGE 312

$\frac{3}{5}$ of the tourists who visit Florida come during the summer. $\frac{3}{10}$ travel to Florida during the winter. During which season does Florida get more tourists?

Understand

1. Underline the question.

2. What fraction of tourists visit Florida in the summer? $\frac{3}{5}$

3. What fraction of tourists visit Florida in the winter? $\frac{3}{10}$

Plan

4. Find a common denominator for $\frac{3}{5}$ and $\frac{3}{10}$. 10

5 Rewrite each fraction using the common denominator. $\frac{6}{10}$, $\frac{3}{10}$

Solve

6. Compare the fractions. Which fraction is greater? $\frac{6}{10}$

7. When do more tourists visit Florida—summer or winter? Summer.

Look Back

8. How could you have solved the problem in a different way?

   Possible answers: Use the strategy Draw a Picture; write both fractions as decimals and compare the decimals.

9. Use your answer to the problem to make a generalization. If two fractions have the same numerator, which is the greater fraction?

   The one with the lesser number in the denominator.

SOLVE ANOTHER PROBLEM

Manny, Anita, and Taylor shared the driving on a trip. Manny drove $\frac{1}{8}$ of the distance. Anita drove $\frac{1}{4}$ of the distance. Did Manny or Anita drive more miles? Explain how you know.

Anita, because $\frac{1}{4}$ is greater than $\frac{1}{8}$.

Name ____________

Guided Problem Solving 6-1

GPS PROBLEM 36, STUDENT PAGE 327

Sandra makes bracelets, necklaces, and chokers using leather string. A bracelet requires $\frac{7}{12}$ ft of string, and a necklace requires $\frac{22}{12}$ ft. She has $\frac{81}{12}$ ft, which is exactly enough to make 3 bracelets, 2 necklaces, and 1 choker. How much string does each choker require? Explain.

Understand

1. Circle what you are asked to find.

2. How much leather string does Sandra have? $\frac{81}{12}$ feet

3. Underline the amount of string needed to make a bracelet and a necklace.

Plan

4. Which operation will you use to find the amount of string needed to make

   3 bracelets? Addition. 2 necklaces? Addition.

5. Which operation will you use to find the string left over after making the bracelets and necklaces? Subtraction.

Solve

6. Write a number sentence showing the amount of string needed to make 3 bracelets. $\frac{7}{12} + \frac{7}{12} + \frac{7}{12} = \frac{21}{12}$

7. How much string is needed to make 2 necklaces? $\frac{44}{12}$ feet

8. How much string is needed to make 3 bracelets and 2 necklaces? $\frac{65}{12}$ feet

9. How much string will Sandra have left to make one choker? Explain. $\frac{16}{12}$ feet

   Find string needed for 3 bracelets and 2 necklaces. String left is amount needed to make 1 choker.

Look Back

10. What other operation could you have used to find the amount of string needed to make 3 bracelets? Multiplication.

SOLVE ANOTHER PROBLEM

Sandra also makes belts. She has $\frac{92}{12}$ feet of string, which is enough to make 2 bracelets, 2 necklaces, and 1 belt. A bracelet requires $\frac{7}{12}$ feet and a necklace requires $\frac{22}{12}$ feet of string. How much string does each belt require? $\frac{34}{12}$ feet

Name ____________________

Guided Problem Solving 6-2

GPS PROBLEM 26, STUDENT PAGE 332

A recipe for fruit punch calls for $\frac{3}{8}$ of a quart of lemon drink, $\frac{3}{2}$ of a quart of orange juice, $\frac{1}{10}$ of a quart of cranberry juice, and $\frac{3}{4}$ of a quart of soda water. How large a container is needed for the punch? Explain.

Understand

Possible answers: Items 7 and 8

1. Underline the quantity for each ingredient in the punch.

Plan

2. What is the least common denominator for the ingredients? 40
3. Write an equivalent fraction using the least common denominator.

   a. $\frac{3}{8}$ $\frac{15}{40}$ b. $\frac{3}{2}$ $\frac{60}{40}$ c. $\frac{1}{10}$ $\frac{4}{40}$ d. $\frac{3}{4}$ $\frac{30}{40}$

4. Which operation will you use to find the total quantity of punch? Addition.
5. Which of the following is a reasonable answer? c

   a. less than 1 qt b. about 1 qt c. more than 1 qt

Solve

6. How much punch does the recipe make? $\frac{109}{40} = 2\frac{29}{40}$ qt
7. Think about how much liquid most pitchers and punch bowls hold. What is a reasonable size container for the punch? Explain. 3 qt; $2\frac{1}{2}$ qt is too small. Other sizes would be too large.

Look Back

8. What should you do if the size container you chose in Item 7 does *not* fall within the range you chose for Item 5? Check estimate and calculations to find errors.

SOLVE ANOTHER PROBLEM

A recipe for party mix calls for $\frac{3}{4}$ of a cup of cereal, $\frac{1}{4}$ of a cup of peanuts, $\frac{5}{8}$ of a cup of pretzels, and $\frac{1}{2}$ of a cup of crackers. How many cups are in the mix? How large a container is needed? Explain. Possible answer: $\frac{17}{8} = 2\frac{1}{8}$ c; $2\frac{1}{2}$ c container since 2 c is too small.

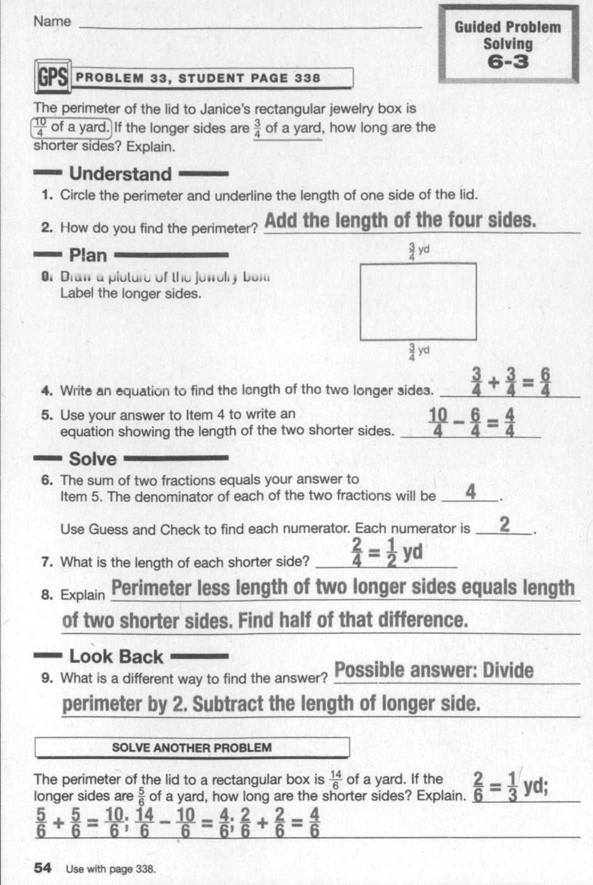

Name ____________________

Guided Problem Solving 6-3

GPS PROBLEM 33, STUDENT PAGE 338

The perimeter of the lid to Janice's rectangular jewelry box is $\frac{10}{4}$ of a yard. If the longer sides are $\frac{3}{4}$ of a yard, how long are the shorter sides? Explain.

Understand

1. Circle the perimeter and underline the length of one side of the lid.
2. How do you find the perimeter? Add the length of the four sides.

Plan

3. Draw a picture of the jewelry box. Label the longer sides.

4. Write an equation to find the length of the two longer sides. $\frac{3}{4} + \frac{3}{4} = \frac{6}{4}$
5. Use your answer to Item 4 to write an equation showing the length of the two shorter sides. $\frac{10}{4} - \frac{6}{4} = \frac{4}{4}$

Solve

6. The sum of two fractions equals your answer to Item 5. The denominator of each of the two fractions will be 4.

   Use Guess and Check to find each numerator. Each numerator is 2.

7. What is the length of each shorter side? $\frac{2}{4} = \frac{1}{2}$ yd
8. Explain Perimeter less length of two longer sides equals length of two shorter sides. Find half of that difference.

Look Back

9. What is a different way to find the answer? Possible answer: Divide perimeter by 2. Subtract the length of longer side.

SOLVE ANOTHER PROBLEM

The perimeter of the lid to a rectangular box is $\frac{14}{6}$ of a yard. If the longer sides are $\frac{5}{6}$ of a yard, how long are the shorter sides? Explain. $\frac{2}{6} = \frac{1}{3}$ yd; $\frac{5}{6} + \frac{5}{6} = \frac{10}{6}$; $\frac{14}{6} - \frac{10}{6} = \frac{4}{6}$; $\frac{2}{6} + \frac{2}{6} = \frac{4}{6}$

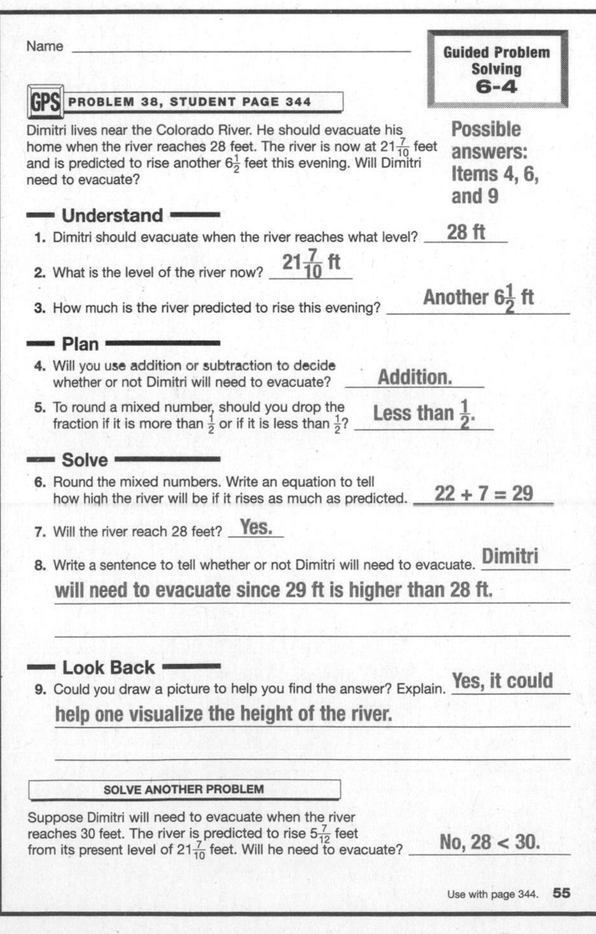

Name ____________________

Guided Problem Solving 6-4

GPS PROBLEM 38, STUDENT PAGE 344

Dimitri lives near the Colorado River. He should evacuate his home when the river reaches 28 feet. The river is now at $21\frac{7}{10}$ feet and is predicted to rise another $6\frac{1}{2}$ feet this evening. Will Dimitri need to evacuate?

Possible answers: Items 4, 6, and 9

Understand

1. Dimitri should evacuate when the river reaches what level? 28 ft
2. What is the level of the river now? $21\frac{7}{10}$ ft
3. How much is the river predicted to rise this evening? Another $6\frac{1}{2}$ ft

Plan

4. Will you use addition or subtraction to decide whether or not Dimitri will need to evacuate? Addition.
5. To round a mixed number, should you drop the fraction if it is more than $\frac{1}{2}$ or if it is less than $\frac{1}{2}$? Less than $\frac{1}{2}$.

Solve

6. Round the mixed numbers. Write an equation to tell how high the river will be if it rises as much as predicted. $22 + 7 = 29$
7. Will the river reach 28 feet? Yes.
8. Write a sentence to tell whether or not Dimitri will need to evacuate. Dimitri will need to evacuate since 29 ft is higher than 28 ft.

Look Back

9. Could you draw a picture to help you find the answer? Explain. Yes, it could help one visualize the height of the river.

SOLVE ANOTHER PROBLEM

Suppose Dimitri will need to evacuate when the river reaches 30 feet. The river is predicted to rise $5\frac{7}{12}$ feet from its present level of $21\frac{7}{10}$ feet. Will he need to evacuate? No, $28 < 30$.

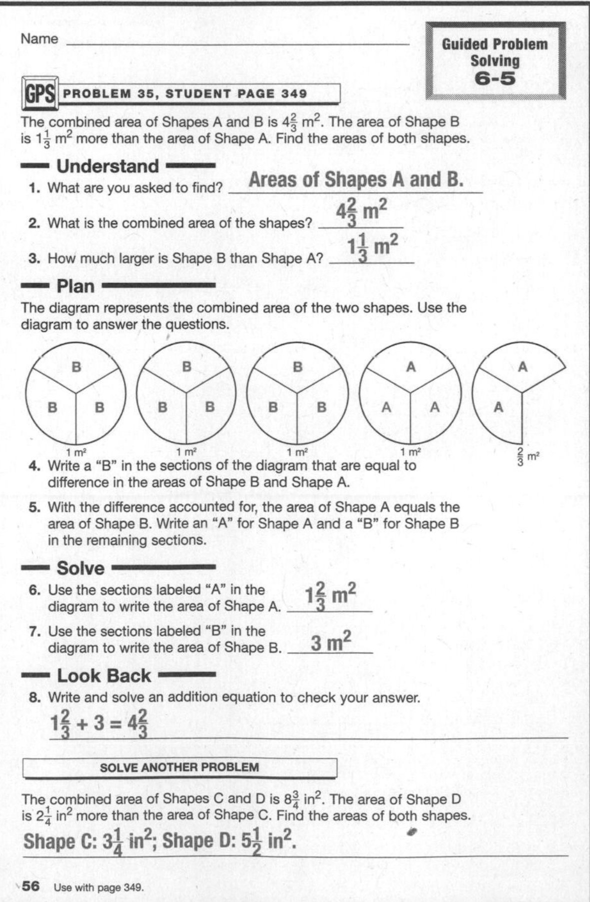

Name ____________________

Guided Problem Solving 6-5

GPS PROBLEM 35, STUDENT PAGE 349

The combined area of Shapes A and B is $4\frac{2}{3}$ m². The area of Shape B is $1\frac{1}{3}$ m² more than the area of Shape A. Find the areas of both shapes.

Understand

1. What are you asked to find? Areas of Shapes A and B.
2. What is the combined area of the shapes? $4\frac{2}{3}$ m²
3. How much larger is Shape B than Shape A? $1\frac{1}{3}$ m²

Plan

The diagram represents the combined area of the two shapes. Use the diagram to answer the questions.

4. Write a "B" in the sections of the diagram that are equal to difference in the areas of Shape B and Shape A.
5. With the difference accounted for, the area of Shape A equals the area of Shape B. Write an "A" for Shape A and a "B" for Shape B in the remaining sections.

Solve

6. Use the sections labeled "A" in the diagram to write the area of Shape A. $1\frac{2}{3}$ m²
7. Use the sections labeled "B" in the diagram to write the area of Shape B. 3 m²

Look Back

8. Write and solve an addition equation to check your answer.

   $1\frac{2}{3} + 3 = 4\frac{2}{3}$

SOLVE ANOTHER PROBLEM

The combined area of Shapes C and D is $8\frac{3}{4}$ in². The area of Shape D is $2\frac{1}{4}$ in² more than the area of Shape C. Find the areas of both shapes.

Shape C: $3\frac{1}{4}$ in²; Shape D: $5\frac{1}{2}$ in².

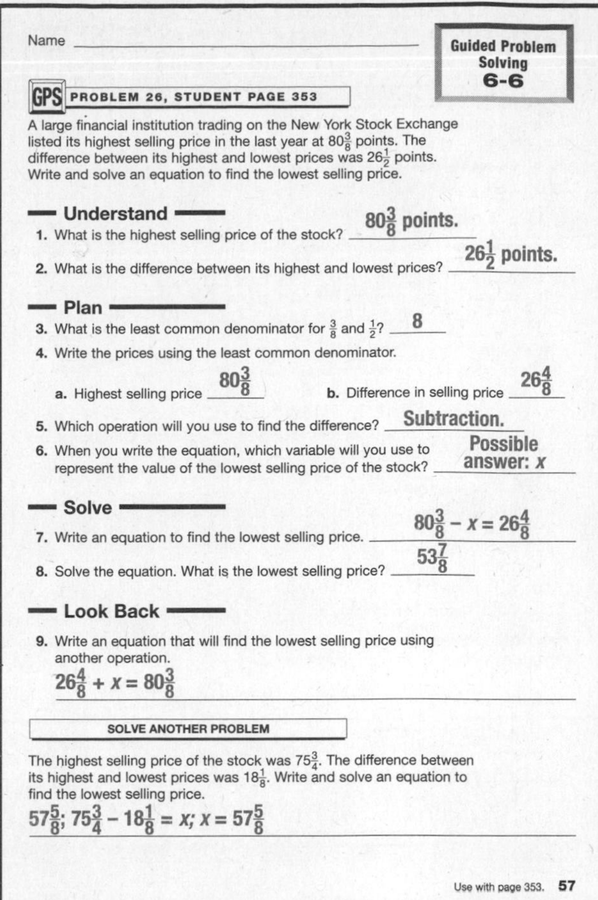

Name ______

Guided Problem Solving 6-6

GPS PROBLEM 26, STUDENT PAGE 353

A large financial institution trading on the New York Stock Exchange listed its highest selling price in the last year at $80\frac{3}{8}$ points. The difference between its highest and lowest prices was $26\frac{1}{2}$ points. Write and solve an equation to find the lowest selling price.

Understand

1. What is the highest selling price of the stock? **$80\frac{3}{8}$ points.**
2. What is the difference between its highest and lowest prices? **$26\frac{1}{2}$ points.**

Plan

3. What is the least common denominator for $\frac{3}{8}$ and $\frac{1}{2}$? **8**
4. Write the prices using the least common denominator.
   a. Highest selling price **$80\frac{3}{8}$** b. Difference in selling price **$26\frac{4}{8}$**
5. Which operation will you use to find the difference? **Subtraction.**
6. When you write the equation, which variable will you use to represent the value of the lowest selling price of the stock? **Possible answer: x**

Solve

7. Write an equation to find the lowest selling price. **$80\frac{3}{8} - x = 26\frac{4}{8}$**
8. Solve the equation. What is the lowest selling price? **$53\frac{7}{8}$**

Look Back

9. Write an equation that will find the lowest selling price using another operation.
   $26\frac{4}{8} + x = 80\frac{3}{8}$

SOLVE ANOTHER PROBLEM

The highest selling price of the stock was $75\frac{3}{4}$. The difference between its highest and lowest prices was $18\frac{1}{8}$. Write and solve an equation to find the lowest selling price.
$57\frac{5}{8}$; $75\frac{3}{4} - 18\frac{1}{8} = x$; $x = 57\frac{5}{8}$

Use with page 353. 57

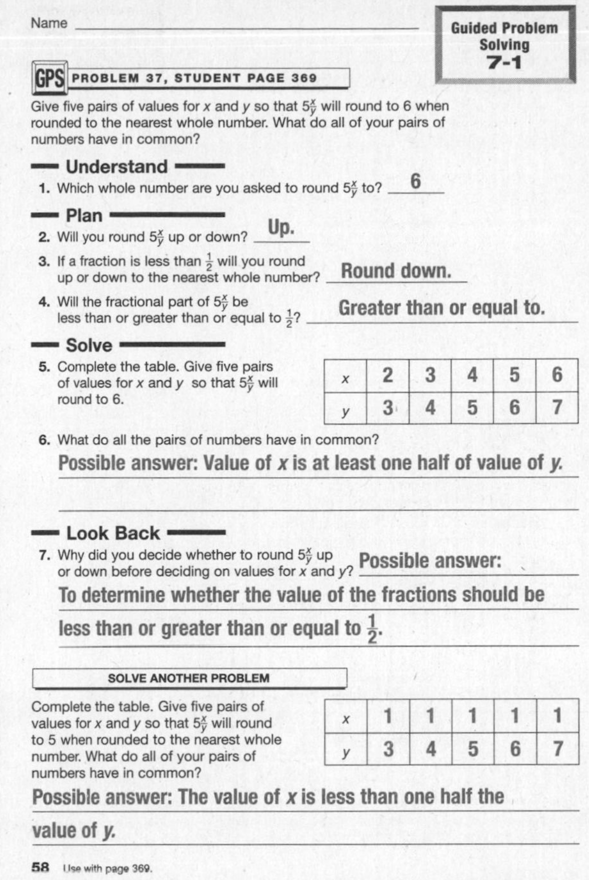

Name ______

Guided Problem Solving 7-1

GPS PROBLEM 37, STUDENT PAGE 369

Give five pairs of values for x and y so that $5\frac{x}{y}$ will round to 6 when rounded to the nearest whole number. What do all of your pairs of numbers have in common?

Understand

1. Which whole number are you asked to round $5\frac{x}{y}$ to? **6**

Plan

2. Will you round $5\frac{x}{y}$ up or down? **Up.**
3. If a fraction is less than $\frac{1}{2}$ will you round up or down to the nearest whole number? **Round down.**
4. Will the fractional part of $5\frac{x}{y}$ be less than or greater than or equal to $\frac{1}{2}$? **Greater than or equal to.**

Solve

5. Complete the table. Give five pairs of values for x and y so that $5\frac{x}{y}$ will round to 6.

x	2	3	4	5	6
y	3	4	5	6	7

6. What do all the pairs of numbers have in common?
   Possible answer: Value of x is at least one half of value of y.

Look Back

7. Why did you decide whether to round $5\frac{x}{y}$ up or down before deciding on values for x and y? **Possible answer: To determine whether the value of the fractions should be less than or greater than or equal to $\frac{1}{2}$.**

SOLVE ANOTHER PROBLEM

Complete the table. Give five pairs of values for x and y so that $5\frac{x}{y}$ will round to 5 when rounded to the nearest whole number. What do all of your pairs of numbers have in common?

x	1	1	1	1	1
y	3	4	5	6	7

Possible answer: The value of x is less than one half the value of y.

58 Use with page 369.

Name ______

Guided Problem Solving 7-2

GPS PROBLEM 36, STUDENT PAGE 374

Castile soap is named for the kingdom of Castile in Spain where the soap was first produced. To make about 36 bars, 1 pound 9 ounces of olive oil is needed. If a pound of olive oil costs \$8.00, how much does the olive oil for this recipe cost? Explain.

Understand

1. Underline what you are asked to find.
2. What is the cost per pound of the olive oil? **\$8.00**
3. How much olive oil is used to make 36 bars of soap? **1 pound 9 ounces**

Plan

4. There are 16 ounces in one pound. How many ounces of olive oil are used to make 36 bars of soap? **25 ounces**
5. Write the quantity of olive oil as an improper fraction. **$\frac{25}{16}$**
6. Write an expression to show how to find the cost of the olive oil used in 36 bars of Castile soap. **$\frac{25}{16} \times 8$**

Solve

7. What is the cost to make 36 bars of soap?. **\$12.50**
8. Explain how you found the answer. **Possible answer: Found number of ounces used and cost per ounce; then multiplied these two amounts.**

Look Back

9. How could you find your answer in a different way? **Possible answer: Find cost of fractional part, $\frac{9}{16} \times 8 = 4.50$. Add to cost of a pound, \$8.**

SOLVE ANOTHER PROBLEM

To make about 72 bars, 3 pounds 2 ounces of olive oil is needed. If a pound of olive oil costs \$9.00, how much does the olive oil for this recipe cost? Round your answer to the nearest cent. Explain.
\$28.13; 3 pounds 2 ounces = 50 ounces; $50 \times \frac{9}{16} = 28.125$.

Use with page 374. 59

Name ______

Guided Problem Solving 7-3

GPS PROBLEM 33, STUDENT PAGE 378

To make $\frac{3}{4}$ cup of powdered-milk paint, you mix $\frac{1}{2}$ cup of powdered nonfat milk and $\frac{1}{2}$ cup of water. Adjust this recipe to make one whole cup of paint. Explain your method.

Possible answers: Items 7, 8

Understand

1. Circle the quantity of paint that is made from the recipe.
2. Underline the quantities of the paint ingredients.

Plan

3. How many fourths are in $\frac{3}{4}$? **Three.**
4. To rewrite the recipe for $\frac{1}{4}$ cup of paint, you could divide each quantity by the number in Item 3 or multiply by **$\frac{1}{3}$**.
5. Once the recipe has been written for $\frac{1}{4}$ cup of paint, you can rewrite it for 1 cup of paint by multiplying each quantity by **4**.

Solve

6. Complete the table for $\frac{1}{4}$ cup of paint. Then use your answer to find the quantities for 1 cup of paint.

Paint (cups)	Milk (cups)	Water (cups)
$\frac{3}{4}$	$\frac{1}{2}$	$\frac{1}{2}$
$\frac{1}{4}$	**$\frac{1}{6}$**	**$\frac{1}{6}$**
1	**$\frac{2}{3}$**	**$\frac{2}{3}$**

7. Explain how you found the quantities.
   Found quantities needed to make $\frac{1}{4}$ cup of paint, used those to find quantities needed for 1 cup of paint.

Look Back

8. Explain how you could use division to rewrite the recipe. **Divide 1 by $\frac{3}{4}$. Then multiply the quotient by amounts of ingredients.**

SOLVE ANOTHER PROBLEM

To make $\frac{3}{4}$ cup of powdered-milk paint, you mix $\frac{1}{2}$ cup of powdered nonfat milk and $\frac{1}{2}$ cup of water. Adjust this recipe to make $1\frac{1}{8}$ cup of paint. Explain your method. **Possible answer: $\frac{3}{4}$ cup each; Find $\frac{1}{8}$ cup: $\frac{1}{6} \times \frac{1}{2} = \frac{1}{12}$; $1\frac{1}{8} = \frac{9}{8}$; $9 \times \frac{1}{12} = \frac{3}{4}$**

60 Use with page 378.

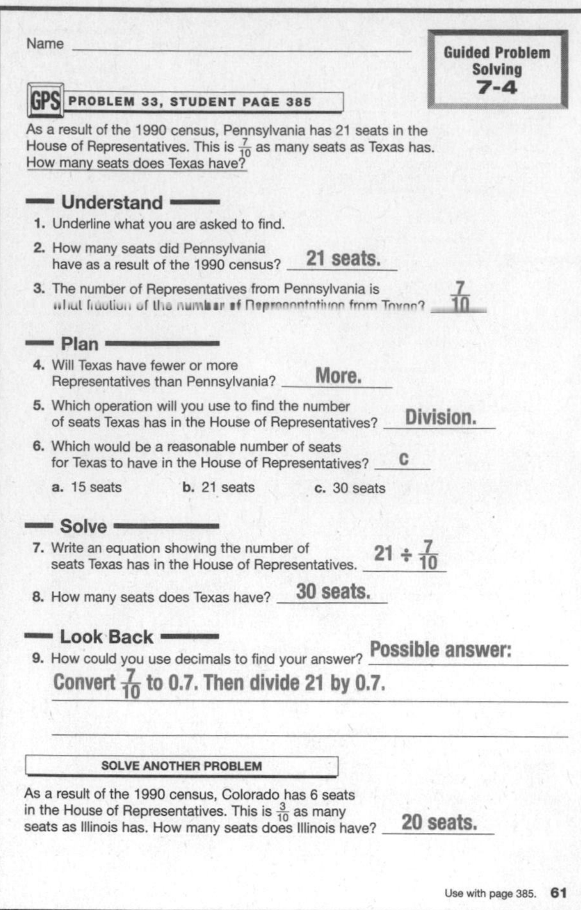

Name ______________________

Guided Problem Solving 7-4

GPS PROBLEM 33, STUDENT PAGE 385

As a result of the 1990 census, Pennsylvania has 21 seats in the House of Representatives. This is $\frac{7}{10}$ as many seats as Texas has. How many seats does Texas have?

— Understand —

1. Underline what you are asked to find.
2. How many seats did Pennsylvania have as a result of the 1990 census? **21 seats.**
3. The number of Representatives from Pennsylvania is what fraction of the number of Representatives from Texas? $\frac{7}{10}$

— Plan —

4. Will Texas have fewer or more Representatives than Pennsylvania? **More.**
5. Which operation will you use to find the number of seats Texas has in the House of Representatives? **Division.**
6. Which would be a reasonable number of seats for Texas to have in the House of Representatives? **c**

   a. 15 seats b. 21 seats c. 30 seats

— Solve —

7. Write an equation showing the number of seats Texas has in the House of Representatives. $21 \div \frac{7}{10}$
8. How many seats does Texas have? **30 seats.**

— Look Back —

9. How could you use decimals to find your answer? **Possible answer: Convert $\frac{7}{10}$ to 0.7. Then divide 21 by 0.7.**

SOLVE ANOTHER PROBLEM

As a result of the 1990 census, Colorado has 6 seats in the House of Representatives. This is $\frac{3}{10}$ as many seats as Illinois has. How many seats does Illinois have? **20 seats.**

Use with page 385. 61

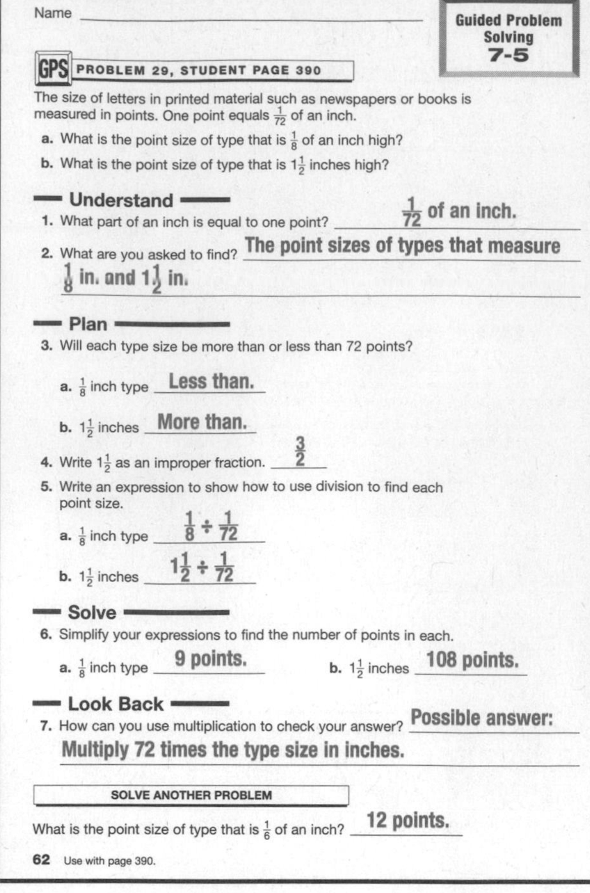

Name ______________________

Guided Problem Solving 7-5

GPS PROBLEM 29, STUDENT PAGE 390

The size of letters in printed material such as newspapers or books is measured in points. One point equals $\frac{1}{72}$ of an inch.

a. What is the point size of type that is $\frac{1}{8}$ of an inch high?

b. What is the point size of type that is $1\frac{1}{2}$ inches high?

— Understand —

1. What part of an inch is equal to one point? **$\frac{1}{72}$ of an inch.**
2. What are you asked to find? **The point sizes of types that measure $\frac{1}{8}$ in. and $1\frac{1}{2}$ in.**

— Plan —

3. Will each type size be more than or less than 72 points?

   a. $\frac{1}{8}$ inch type **Less than.**

   b. $1\frac{1}{2}$ inches **More than.**
4. Write $1\frac{1}{2}$ as an improper fraction. $\frac{3}{2}$
5. Write an expression to show how to use division to find each point size.

   a. $\frac{1}{8}$ inch type $\frac{1}{8} \div \frac{1}{72}$

   b. $1\frac{1}{2}$ inches $1\frac{1}{2} \div \frac{1}{72}$

— Solve —

6. Simplify your expressions to find the number of points in each.

   a. $\frac{1}{8}$ inch type **9 points.** b. $1\frac{1}{2}$ inches **108 points.**

— Look Back —

7. How can you use multiplication to check your answer? **Possible answer: Multiply 72 times the type size in inches.**

SOLVE ANOTHER PROBLEM

What is the point size of type that is $\frac{1}{6}$ of an inch? **12 points.**

62 Use with page 390.

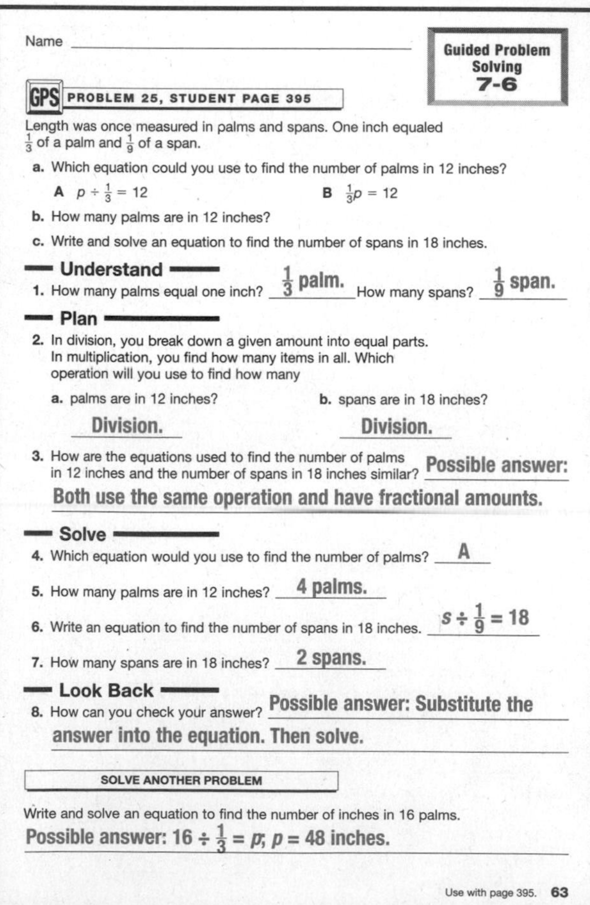

Name ______________________

Guided Problem Solving 7-6

GPS PROBLEM 25, STUDENT PAGE 395

Length was once measured in palms and spans. One inch equaled $\frac{1}{3}$ of a palm and $\frac{1}{9}$ of a span.

a. Which equation could you use to find the number of palms in 12 inches?

   A $p \div \frac{1}{3} = 12$ **B** $\frac{1}{3}p = 12$

b. How many palms are in 12 inches?

c. Write and solve an equation to find the number of spans in 18 inches.

— Understand —

1. How many palms equal one inch? **$\frac{1}{3}$ palm.** How many spans? **$\frac{1}{9}$ span.**

— Plan —

2. In division, you break down a given amount into equal parts. In multiplication, you find how many items in all. Which operation will you use to find how many

   a. palms are in 12 inches? **Division.** b. spans are in 18 inches? **Division.**
3. How are the equations used to find the number of palms in 12 inches and the number of spans in 18 inches similar? **Possible answer: Both use the same operation and have fractional amounts.**

— Solve —

4. Which equation would you use to find the number of palms? **A**
5. How many palms are in 12 inches? **4 palms.**
6. Write an equation to find the number of spans in 18 inches. $s \div \frac{1}{9} = 18$
7. How many spans are in 18 inches? **2 spans.**

— Look Back —

8. How can you check your answer? **Possible answer: Substitute the answer into the equation. Then solve.**

SOLVE ANOTHER PROBLEM

Write and solve an equation to find the number of inches in 16 palms.

Possible answer: $16 \div \frac{1}{3} = p$; $p = 48$ inches.

Use with page 395. 63

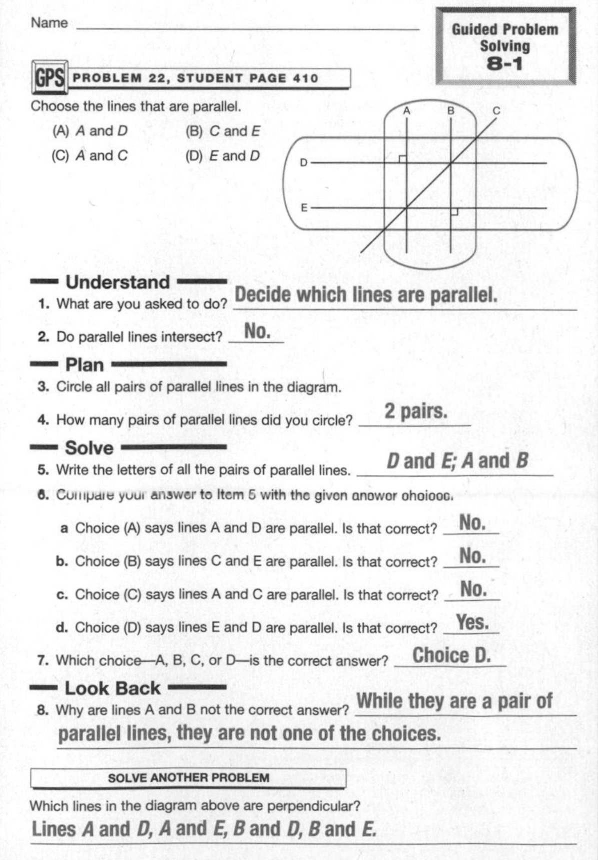

Name ______________________

Guided Problem Solving 8-1

GPS PROBLEM 22, STUDENT PAGE 410

Choose the lines that are parallel.

(A) *A* and *D* (B) *C* and *E*

(C) *A* and *C* (D) *E* and *D*

— Understand —

1. What are you asked to do? **Decide which lines are parallel.**
2. Do parallel lines intersect? **No.**

— Plan —

3. Circle all pairs of parallel lines in the diagram.
4. How many pairs of parallel lines did you circle? **2 pairs.**

— Solve —

5. Write the letters of all the pairs of parallel lines. ***D* and *E*; *A* and *B***
6. Compare your answer to Item 5 with the given answer choices.

   a. Choice (A) says lines A and D are parallel. Is that correct? **No.**

   b. Choice (B) says lines C and E are parallel. Is that correct? **No.**

   c. Choice (C) says lines A and C are parallel. Is that correct? **No.**

   d. Choice (D) says lines E and D are parallel. Is that correct? **Yes.**
7. Which choice—A, B, C, or D—is the correct answer? **Choice D.**

— Look Back —

8. Why are lines A and B not the correct answer? **While they are a pair of parallel lines, they are not one of the choices.**

SOLVE ANOTHER PROBLEM

Which lines in the diagram above are perpendicular?

Lines *A* and *D*, *A* and *E*, *B* and *D*, *B* and *E*.

64 Use with page 410.

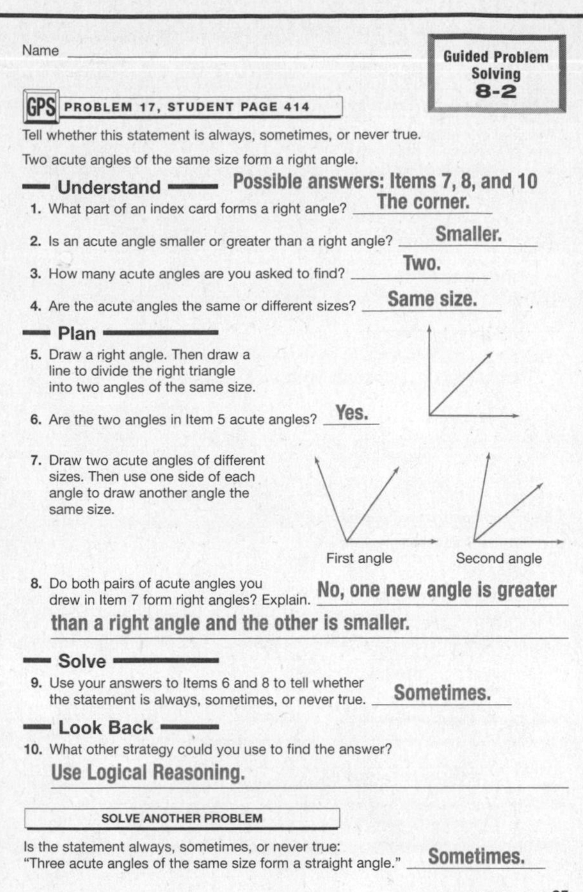

Name ______________________

Guided Problem Solving 8-2

GPS **PROBLEM 17, STUDENT PAGE 414**

Tell whether this statement is always, sometimes, or never true.

Two acute angles of the same size form a right angle.

Understand

Possible answers: Items 7, 8, and 10

1. What part of an index card forms a right angle? The corner.
2. Is an acute angle smaller or greater than a right angle? Smaller.
3. How many acute angles are you asked to find? Two.
4. Are the acute angles the same or different sizes? Same size.

Plan

5. Draw a right angle. Then draw a line to divide the right triangle into two angles of the same size.
6. Are the two angles in Item 5 acute angles? Yes.
7. Draw two acute angles of different sizes. Then use one side of each angle to draw another angle the same size.

First angle — Second angle

8. Do both pairs of acute angles you drew in Item 7 form right angles? Explain. No, one new angle is greater than a right angle and the other is smaller.

Solve

9. Use your answers to Items 6 and 8 to tell whether the statement is always, sometimes, or never true. Sometimes.

Look Back

10. What other strategy could you use to find the answer? Use Logical Reasoning.

SOLVE ANOTHER PROBLEM

Is the statement always, sometimes, or never true: "Three acute angles of the same size form a straight angle." Sometimes.

Name ______________________

Guided Problem Solving 8-3

GPS **PROBLEM 29, STUDENT PAGE 420**

Estimate the measurement of the obtuse angle.

(A) 45° (B) 135°

(C) 90° (D) 270°za

Understand

1. What is the definition of an obtuse angle? An angle with a measure between 90° and 180°.
2. Which of these kinds of angles are shown in the diagram? C

 a. acute and right b. right and obtuse c. acute and obtuse

Plan

3. Darken the rays that make up the obtuse angle in the diagram.
4. Classify the type of angle given in each choice as acute, obtuse, right, or none of these.

 a. Choice A (45°) Acute. b. Choice B (135°) Obtuse.

 c. Choice C (90°) Right. d. Choice D (270°) None.

Solve

5. Which choice is an obtuse angle? Choice B.

Look Back

6. Why does classifying the angle help estimate the measure? Possible answer: The classification narrows the range of measurement.

SOLVE ANOTHER PROBLEM

Which of the answer choices is a reasonable estimate for the measurement of the acute angle in the drawing above? Choice A.

(A) 45° (B) 135°

(C) 90° (D) 270°

Name ______________________

Guided Problem Solving 8-4

GPS **PROBLEM 41, STUDENT PAGE 427**

A triangle has angles *A*, *B*, and *C*. The complement of ∠*A* is 58° and the supplement of ∠*B* is 60°. What is the measure of ∠*C*? Explain your strategy.

Understand

1. Which angle's measurement are you to find? ∠C
2. Underline the information you need.

Plan

3. What is sum of the measures of two complementary angles? 90°
4. The complement of ∠*A* is 58°. What is the measure of ∠*A*? 32°
5. What is sum of the measures of two supplementary angles? 180°
6. The supplement of ∠*B* is 60°. What is the measure of ∠*B*? 120°
7. What is sum of the measures of the three angles in a triangle? 180°

Solve

8. Add the measurements of ∠*A* and ∠*B*: 32° + 120° = 152°
9. Find the measure of ∠*C*: 180° − 152° = 28°
10. What is the measure of ∠*C*? 28°
11. What strategy did you use to find the measure of ∠*C*? Possible answer: Use Logical Reasoning.

Look Back

12. What other strategies could you use to find the measure of ∠*C*? Possible answers: Draw a Diagram. Solve a Simpler Problem.

SOLVE ANOTHER PROBLEM

A triangle has angles *D*, *E*, and *F*. The complement of ∠*D* is 42° and the supplement of ∠*E* is 54°. What is the measure of ∠*F*? 6°

Name ______________________

Guided Problem Solving 8-5

GPS **PROBLEM 29, STUDENT PAGE 431**

Jeremy has two poles for the end of his tent. They are each 4 feet long. Can he form the triangular end of his tent if he puts two pole ends together and places the other ends 9 feet apart?

Understand

1. What figure will be formed by the two poles and the ground? Triangle.
2. What are the lengths of each of the two poles? 4 feet.
3. How far apart will Jeremy place the ends of the poles? 9 feet.

Plan

4. Is the sum of the two shorter sides of a triangle greater or less than the length of the longer side? Greater than.
5. What is the length of the longest side of the figure formed? 9 feet.
6. Write an equation to find the sum of the two shorter tent poles? 4 + 4 = 8

Solve

7. Is the sum in Item 6 greater than or less than the length of the longest side? Less than.
8. Can Jeremy place the poles 9 feet apart? No.

Look Back

9. What other strategy could you use to find the answer? Possible answer: Draw a diagram.

SOLVE ANOTHER PROBLEM

Diana has two poles for the end of her tent. They are each 8 feet long. Can she form the triangular end of her tent if she puts two pole ends together and places the other ends 10 feet apart? Explain.

Yes, the sum of the shorter sides is 16. Since 16 is greater than 10, the poles could form a triangle.

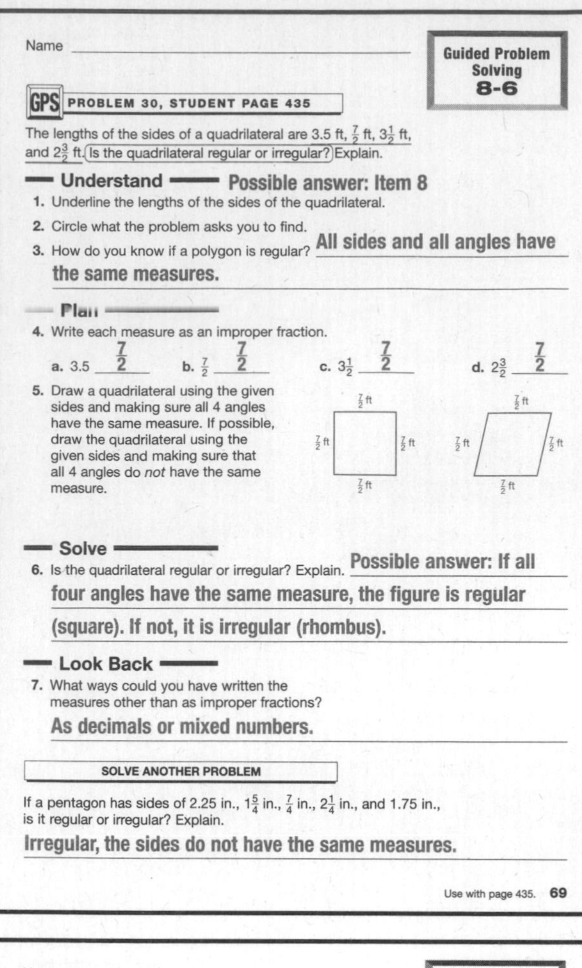

Name ______________________

Guided Problem Solving 8-6

GPS PROBLEM 30, STUDENT PAGE 435

The lengths of the sides of a quadrilateral are 3.5 ft, $\frac{7}{2}$ ft, $3\frac{1}{2}$ ft, and $2\frac{3}{2}$ ft. Is the quadrilateral regular or irregular? Explain.

Understand Possible answer: Item 8

1. Underline the lengths of the sides of the quadrilateral.
2. Circle what the problem asks you to find.
3. How do you know if a polygon is regular? All sides and all angles have the same measures.

Plan

4. Write each measure as an improper fraction.

   a. 3.5 $\frac{7}{2}$ b. $\frac{7}{2}$ $\frac{7}{2}$ c. $3\frac{1}{2}$ $\frac{7}{2}$ d. $2\frac{3}{2}$ $\frac{7}{2}$

5. Draw a quadrilateral using the given sides and making sure all 4 angles have the same measure. If possible, draw the quadrilateral using the given sides and making sure that all 4 angles do *not* have the same measure.

Solve

6. Is the quadrilateral regular or irregular? Explain. Possible answer: If all four angles have the same measure, the figure is regular (square). If not, it is irregular (rhombus).

Look Back

7. What ways could you have written the measures other than as improper fractions? As decimals or mixed numbers.

SOLVE ANOTHER PROBLEM

If a pentagon has sides of 2.25 in., $1\frac{5}{4}$ in., $\frac{7}{4}$ in., $2\frac{1}{4}$ in., and 1.75 in., is it regular or irregular? Explain.

Irregular, the sides do not have the same measures.

Use with page 435. 69

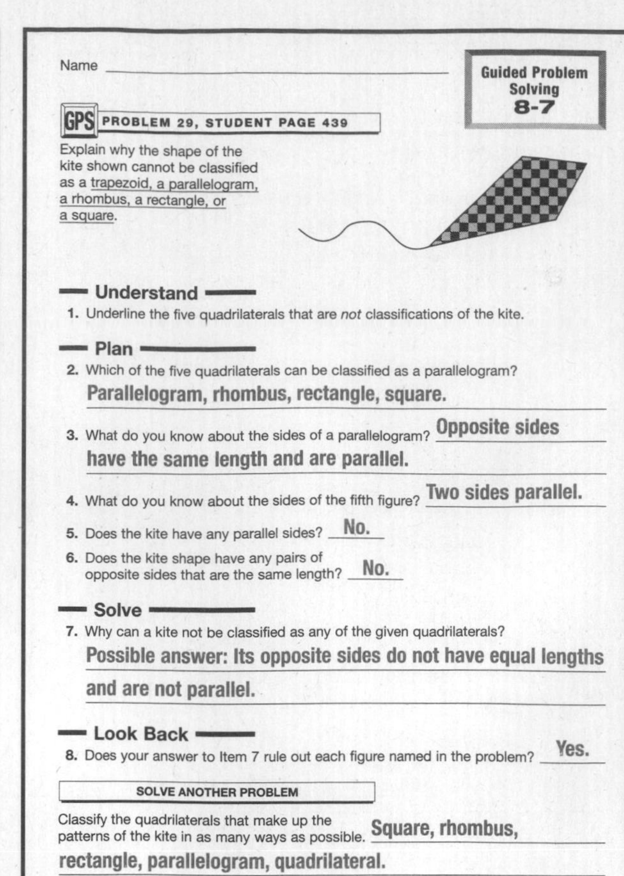

Name ______________________

Guided Problem Solving 8-7

GPS PROBLEM 29, STUDENT PAGE 439

Explain why the shape of the kite shown cannot be classified as a trapezoid, a parallelogram, a rhombus, a rectangle, or a square.

Understand

1. Underline the five quadrilaterals that are *not* classifications of the kite.

Plan

2. Which of the five quadrilaterals can be classified as a parallelogram? Parallelogram, rhombus, rectangle, square.
3. What do you know about the sides of a parallelogram? Opposite sides have the same length and are parallel.
4. What do you know about the sides of the fifth figure? Two sides parallel.
5. Does the kite have any parallel sides? No.
6. Does the kite shape have any pairs of opposite sides that are the same length? No.

Solve

7. Why can a kite not be classified as any of the given quadrilaterals? Possible answer: Its opposite sides do not have equal lengths and are not parallel.

Look Back

8. Does your answer to Item 7 rule out each figure named in the problem? Yes.

SOLVE ANOTHER PROBLEM

Classify the quadrilaterals that make up the patterns of the kite in as many ways as possible. Square, rhombus, rectangle, parallelogram, quadrilateral.

70 Use with page 439.

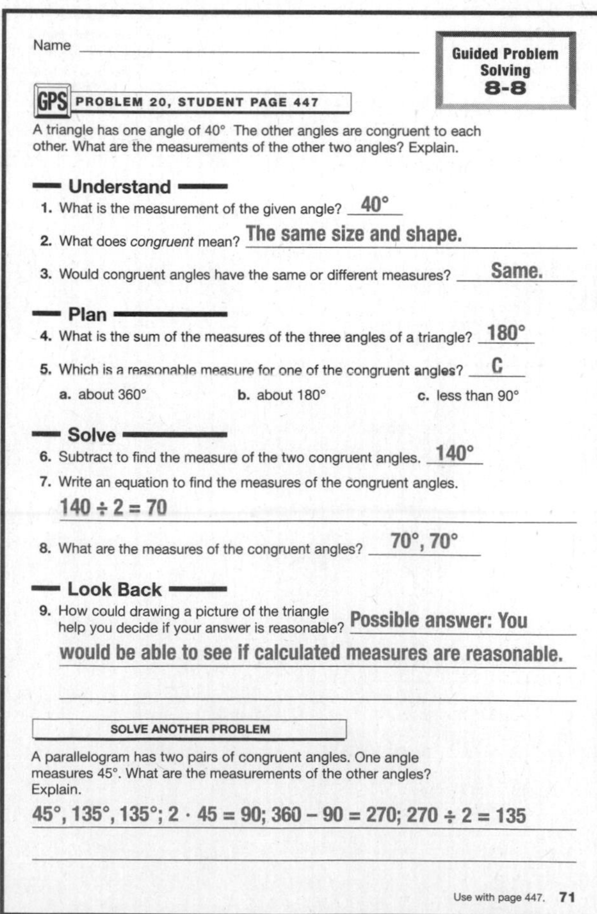

Name ______________________

Guided Problem Solving 8-8

GPS PROBLEM 20, STUDENT PAGE 447

A triangle has one angle of 40° The other angles are congruent to each other. What are the measurements of the other two angles? Explain.

Understand

1. What is the measurement of the given angle? 40°
2. What does *congruent* mean? The same size and shape.
3. Would congruent angles have the same or different measures? Same.

Plan

4. What is the sum of the measures of the three angles of a triangle? 180°
5. Which is a reasonable measure for one of the congruent angles? C

   a. about 360° b. about 180° c. less than 90°

Solve

6. Subtract to find the measure of the two congruent angles. 140°
7. Write an equation to find the measures of the congruent angles. 140 ÷ 2 = 70
8. What are the measures of the congruent angles? 70°, 70°

Look Back

9. How could drawing a picture of the triangle help you decide if your answer is reasonable? Possible answer: You would be able to see if calculated measures are reasonable.

SOLVE ANOTHER PROBLEM

A parallelogram has two pairs of congruent angles. One angle measures 45°. What are the measurements of the other angles? Explain.

45°, 135°, 135°; 2 · 45 = 90; 360 − 90 = 270; 270 ÷ 2 = 135

Use with page 447. 71

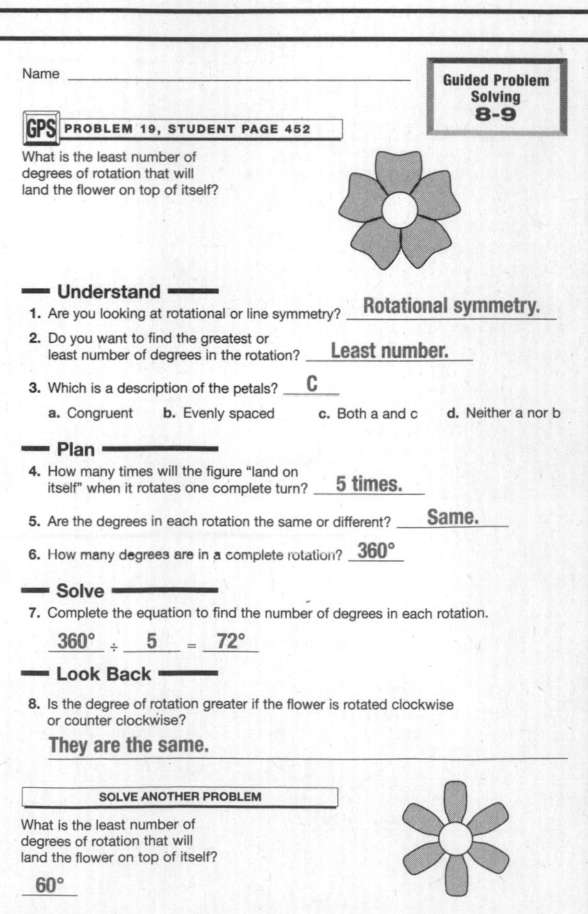

Name ______________________

Guided Problem Solving 8-9

GPS PROBLEM 19, STUDENT PAGE 452

What is the least number of degrees of rotation that will land the flower on top of itself?

Understand

1. Are you looking at rotational or line symmetry? Rotational symmetry.
2. Do you want to find the greatest or least number of degrees in the rotation? Least number.
3. Which is a description of the petals? C

   a. Congruent b. Evenly spaced c. Both a and c d. Neither a nor b

Plan

4. How many times will the figure "land on itself" when it rotates one complete turn? 5 times.
5. Are the degrees in each rotation the same or different? Same.
6. How many degrees are in a complete rotation? 360°

Solve

7. Complete the equation to find the number of degrees in each rotation.

   360° ÷ 5 = 72°

Look Back

8. Is the degree of rotation greater if the flower is rotated clockwise or counter clockwise? They are the same.

SOLVE ANOTHER PROBLEM

What is the least number of degrees of rotation that will land the flower on top of itself?

60°

72 Use with page 452.

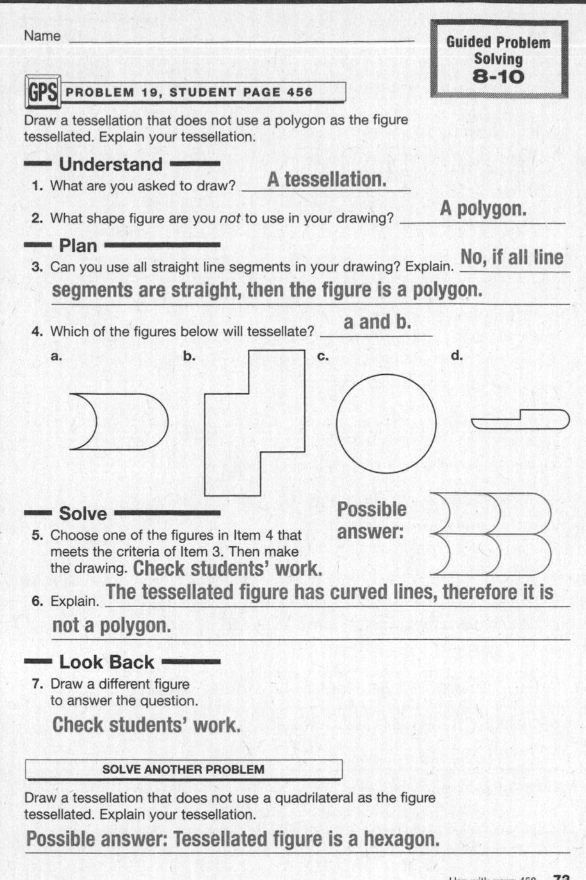

Name ______

Guided Problem Solving 8-10

GPS **PROBLEM 19, STUDENT PAGE 456**

Draw a tessellation that does not use a polygon as the figure tessellated. Explain your tessellation.

Understand

1. What are you asked to draw? A tessellation.
2. What shape figure are you *not* to use in your drawing? A polygon.

Plan

3. Can you use all straight line segments in your drawing? Explain. No, if all line segments are straight, then the figure is a polygon.
4. Which of the figures below will tessellate? a and b.

a. b. c. d.

Solve

5. Choose one of the figures in Item 4 that meets the criteria of Item 3. Then make the drawing. Check students' work.

Possible answer:

6. Explain. The tessellated figure has curved lines, therefore it is not a polygon.

Look Back

7. Draw a different figure to answer the question.

Check students' work.

SOLVE ANOTHER PROBLEM

Draw a tessellation that does not use a quadrilateral as the figure tessellated. Explain your tessellation.

Possible answer: Tessellated figure is a hexagon.

Use with page 456. 73

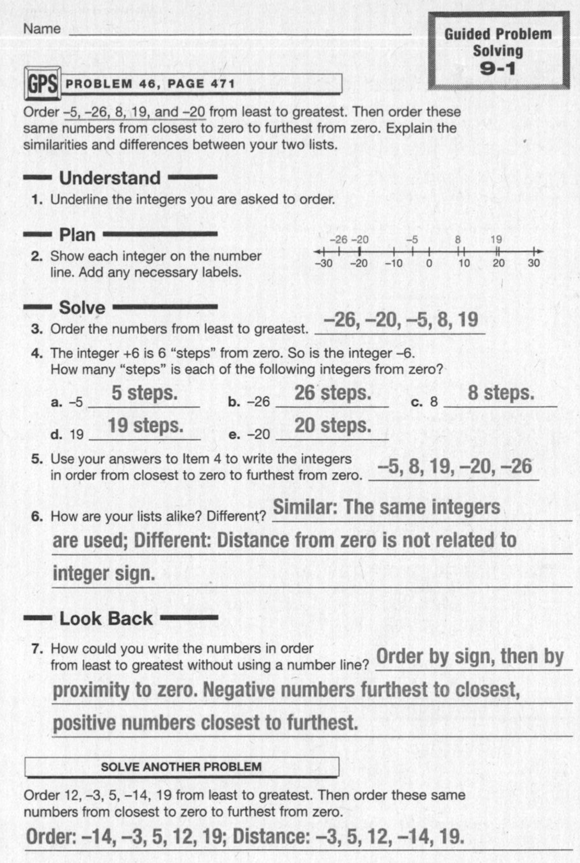

Name ______

Guided Problem Solving 9-1

GPS **PROBLEM 46, PAGE 471**

Order –5, –26, 8, 19, and –20 from least to greatest. Then order these same numbers from closest to zero to furthest from zero. Explain the similarities and differences between your two lists.

Understand

1. Underline the integers you are asked to order.

Plan

2. Show each integer on the number line. Add any necessary labels.

Solve

3. Order the numbers from least to greatest. –26, –20, –5, 8, 19
4. The integer +6 is 6 "steps" from zero. So is the integer –6. How many "steps" is each of the following integers from zero?

a. –5 5 steps. b. –26 26 steps. c. 8 8 steps.

d. 19 19 steps. e. –20 20 steps.

5. Use your answers to Item 4 to write the integers in order from closest to zero to furthest from zero. –5, 8, 19, –20, –26
6. How are your lists alike? Different? Similar: The same integers are used; Different: Distance from zero is not related to integer sign.

Look Back

7. How could you write the numbers in order from least to greatest without using a number line? Order by sign, then by proximity to zero. Negative numbers furthest to closest, positive numbers closest to furthest.

SOLVE ANOTHER PROBLEM

Order 12, –3, 5, –14, 19 from least to greatest. Then order these same numbers from closest to zero to furthest from zero.

Order: –14, –3, 5, 12, 19; Distance: –3, 5, 12, –14, 19.

74 Use with page 471.

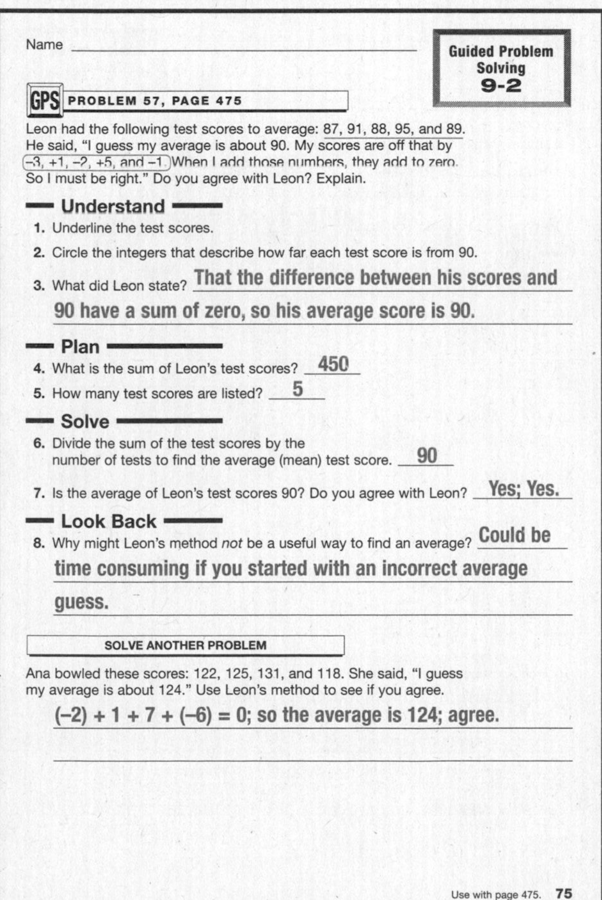

Name ______

Guided Problem Solving 9-2

GPS **PROBLEM 57, PAGE 475**

Leon had the following test scores to average: 87, 91, 88, 95, and 89. He said, "I guess my average is about 90. My scores are off that by –3, +1, –2, +5, and –1. When I add those numbers, they add to zero. So I must be right." Do you agree with Leon? Explain.

Understand

1. Underline the test scores.
2. Circle the integers that describe how far each test score is from 90.
3. What did Leon state? That the difference between his scores and 90 have a sum of zero, so his average score is 90.

Plan

4. What is the sum of Leon's test scores? 450
5. How many test scores are listed? 5

Solve

6. Divide the sum of the test scores by the number of tests to find the average (mean) test score. 90
7. Is the average of Leon's test scores 90? Do you agree with Leon? Yes; Yes.

Look Back

8. Why might Leon's method *not* be a useful way to find an average? Could be time consuming if you started with an incorrect average guess.

SOLVE ANOTHER PROBLEM

Ana bowled these scores: 122, 125, 131, and 118. She said, "I guess my average is about 124." Use Leon's method to see if you agree.

(–2) + 1 + 7 + (–6) = 0; so the average is 124; agree.

Use with page 475. 75

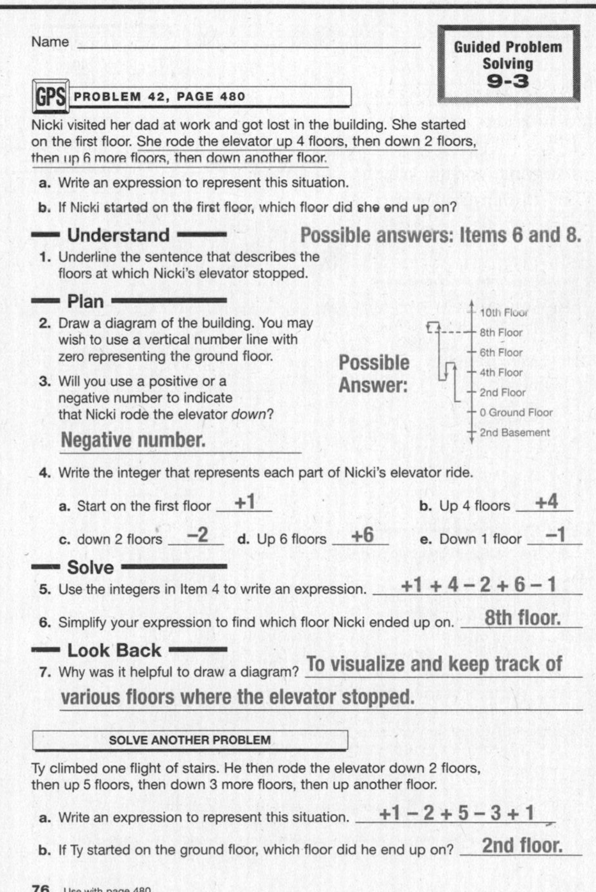

Name ______

Guided Problem Solving 9-3

GPS **PROBLEM 42, PAGE 480**

Nicki visited her dad at work and got lost in the building. She started on the first floor. She rode the elevator up 4 floors, then down 2 floors, then up 6 more floors, then down another floor.

a. Write an expression to represent this situation.

b. If Nicki started on the first floor, which floor did she end up on?

Understand

Possible answers: Items 6 and 8.

1. Underline the sentence that describes the floors at which Nicki's elevator stopped.

Plan

2. Draw a diagram of the building. You may wish to use a vertical number line with zero representing the ground floor.
3. Will you use a positive or a negative number to indicate that Nicki rode the elevator *down*?

Possible Answer:

Negative number.

4. Write the integer that represents each part of Nicki's elevator ride.

a. Start on the first floor +1 b. Up 4 floors +4

c. down 2 floors –2 d. Up 6 floors +6 e. Down 1 floor –1

Solve

5. Use the integers in Item 4 to write an expression. +1 + 4 – 2 + 6 – 1
6. Simplify your expression to find which floor Nicki ended up on. 8th floor.

Look Back

7. Why was it helpful to draw a diagram? To visualize and keep track of various floors where the elevator stopped.

SOLVE ANOTHER PROBLEM

Ty climbed one flight of stairs. He then rode the elevator down 2 floors, then up 5 floors, then down 3 more floors, then up another floor.

a. Write an expression to represent this situation. +1 – 2 + 5 – 3 + 1

b. If Ty started on the ground floor, which floor did he end up on? 2nd floor.

76 Use with page 480.

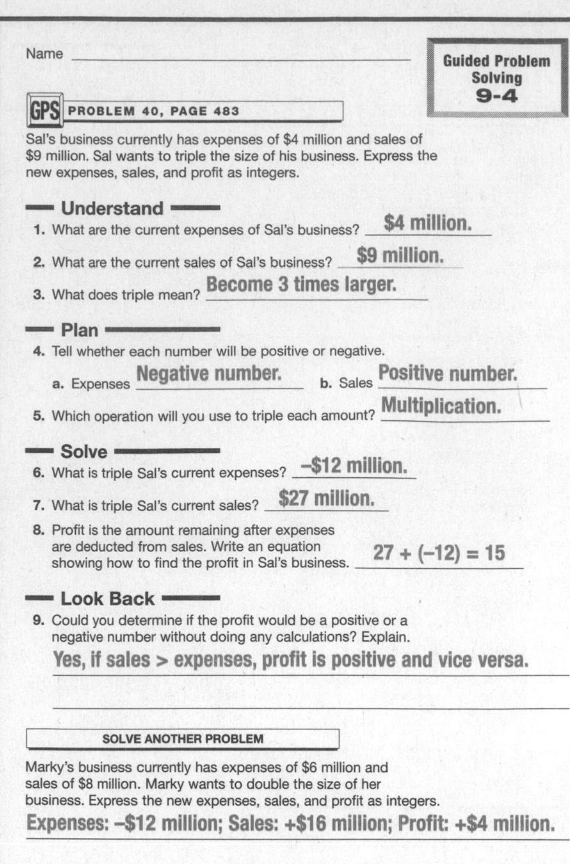

Name ______________________

Guided Problem Solving 9-4

GPS PROBLEM 40, PAGE 483

Sal's business currently has expenses of $4 million and sales of $9 million. Sal wants to triple the size of his business. Express the new expenses, sales, and profit as integers.

Understand

1. What are the current expenses of Sal's business? **$4 million.**
2. What are the current sales of Sal's business? **$9 million.**
3. What does triple mean? **Become 3 times larger.**

Plan

4. Tell whether each number will be positive or negative.
   a. Expenses **Negative number.** b. Sales **Positive number.**
5. Which operation will you use to triple each amount? **Multiplication.**

Solve

6. What is triple Sal's current expenses? **–$12 million.**
7. What is triple Sal's current sales? **$27 million.**
8. Profit is the amount remaining after expenses are deducted from sales. Write an equation showing how to find the profit in Sal's business. **27 + (–12) = 15**

Look Back

9. Could you determine if the profit would be a positive or a negative number without doing any calculations? Explain.
   Yes, if sales > expenses, profit is positive and vice versa.

SOLVE ANOTHER PROBLEM

Marky's business currently has expenses of $6 million and sales of $8 million. Marky wants to double the size of her business. Express the new expenses, sales, and profit as integers.

Expenses: –$12 million; Sales: +$16 million; Profit: +$4 million.

Name ______________________

Guided Problem Solving 9-5

GPS PROBLEM 34, PAGE 491

Use the map and the directions given to find the coordinates of Smallville School.

The school and the marketplace have the same y-coordinate. The x-coordinate of the school is twice the difference between the y-coordinate of the marketplace and the y-coordinate of the gas station.

Smallville, USA

A Marketplace
B Gas Station
C Library
D Post Office
E Willow tree

Understand

1. Circle the phrase that tells how to find the y-coordinate of the school.
2. Underline the phrase that tells how to find the x-coordinate of the school.

Plan

3. Which operations will you use to find the x-coordinate of the school? **b**
   a. Multiplication, then subtraction b. Subtraction, then multiplication
4. The coordinates of the point for the marketplace are **(2, 8)**
5. The coordinates of the points for gas station are **(3, 3)**

Solve

6. What is the y-coordinate of the ordered pair in Item 4? **8**
7. Use the y-coordinates of the ordered pairs you wrote in Items 4 and 5 to write an equation for the x-coordinate of the school. **2 (8 – 3) = 10**
8. What are the coordinates of the school? **(10, 8)**

Look Back

9. Would it have been easier to find the answer by only writing the value of the y-coordinate for each building? Explain. **Possible answer:**
   No, it would be more difficult to keep the data organized.

SOLVE ANOTHER PROBLEM

Use the map above and these directions to find the coordinates of the park.

The park and the library have the same x-coordinate. The y-coordinate of the park is one half the sum of the x-coordinate of the post office and the x-coordinate of the library. **(7, 5)**

Name ______________________

Guided Problem Solving 9-6

GPS PROBLEM 19, PAGE 496

One item that Cheryl had to find on a treasure hunt was located at the point (3, 4) on the map. When Cheryl got there, she realized she had the map upside down. How many units left, right, up, and down on the map should Cheryl walk to find the correct location?

Possible answers: Items 5, 8, and 9

Understand

1. Underline what you are asked to find.
2. Why was Cheryl not at those coordinates? **She read map upside down.**

Plan

3. Mark (3, 4) on the coordinate plane. Label it A.
4. Turn this page upside down. Imagine that the graph was scaled in the usual way. Then mark (3, 4). Label it B.
5. Turn your page to original position. Follow the grid lines to mark the shortest path between the B and A.

Solve

6. Does your path go up or down? How many units? **Up; 8 units.**
7. Does your path go left or right? How many units? **Right; 6 units.**

Look Back

8. Are there other paths that you could choose? Explain. **Yes, for example, one path could start out going right, then up.**
9. What is the relationship between the of number of units the path takes and the original coordinates? **The path is two times the value of each coordinate.**

SOLVE ANOTHER PROBLEM

One item that Norm had to find on a treasure hunt was located at the point (–2, 5) on the map. When Norm got there, he realized he had the map upside down. How many units left, right, up, and down on the map should Norm walk to find the correct location? **Up 10, Left 4.**

Name ______________________

Guided Problem Solving 9-7

GPS PROBLEM 37, PAGE 502

Graph the equations $y = x + 3$ and $y = x + (-3)$ on the same coordinate plane. Describe the relationship between the lines.

Possible answers: Items 5 and 6

Understand

1. Will you graph the equations on one or two coordinates planes? **One.**
2. What are you asked to describe? **The relationship between two lines.**

Plan

3. Complete the T-tables to find some values of x and y for each equation.

$y = x + 3$

x	y
–1	**2**
0	**3**
1	**4**
2	**5**

$y = x + (-3)$

x	y
–1	**–4**
0	**–3**
1	**–2**
2	**–1**

$y = -3x$ $y = 3x$ $y = x + 3$ $y = x + (-3)$

Solve

4. Graph each equation. Label each line.
5. What is the relationship between the lines? **They are parallel.**

Look Back

6. Do you think you would get the same result for the equations $y = x - 3$ and $y = x - (-3)$? Explain. **Yes, these are the opposites of the two equations graphed.**

SOLVE ANOTHER PROBLEM

Graph the equations $y = 3x$ and $y = -3x$ on the coordinate plane above. Label each line. Describe the relationship between the lines.

Possible answer: They intersect at the origin, have an "X" shape, are symmetrical.

Name ______________________

Guided Problem Solving 10-1

GPS PROBLEM 11, PAGE 516

Fire engines carry fire hoses. Fire trucks carry mainly ladders and fire-fighting equipment other than hoses. At one point, the city of San Francisco had 40 fire engines and 18 fire trucks.

a. Give the ratio of fire engines to fire trucks in lowest terms.

b. Give the ratio of fire trucks to total fire vehicles in lowest terms.

Understand

1. How many fire *engines* did the city of San Francisco have? **40 engines.**
2. How many fire *trucks* did the city of San Francisco have? **18 trucks.**

Plan

3. How will you find the total number of fire vehicles in San Francisco? **Add number of fire engines and number of fire trucks.**
4. What is the total number of fire vehicles in San Francisco? **58 vehicles.**

Solve

5. What is the ratio of fire engines to fire trucks? **40:18**
6. Write your ratio in Item 5 in lowest terms, if possible. **20:9**
7. What is the ratio of fire trucks to total fire vehicles? **18:58**
8. Write your ratio in Item 7 in lowest terms, if possible. **9:29**

Look Back

9. How can you tell if the ratio is in lowest terms? **Possible answer: Numerator and denominator have no common factor.**

SOLVE ANOTHER PROBLEM

Use the fire vehicle data above to write each ratio in lowest terms.

a. What is the ratio of fire trucks to fire engines? **9:20**

b. What is the ratio of fire vehicles to fire engines? **29:20**

Name ______________________

Guided Problem Solving 10-2

GPS PROBLEM 23, PAGE 521

The circle graph shows the number of colored beads used in a hand-beaded bracelet. Carole wants to make a smaller bracelet using the same ratios of colors. Draw a circle graph that shows how many beads of each color Carole could use.

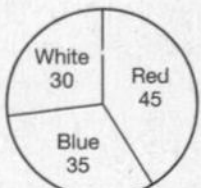

Understand

1. In the circle graph above, how many beads are a. white? **30 beads.** b. blue? **35 beads.** c. red? **45 beads.** d. there in all? **110 beads.**

Plan

2. Equal ratios can help find the number of beads in the smaller bracelet. Will you multiply or divide to find the equal ratios? **Divide.**
3. Write the ratio of blue beads to total beads. Then write an equal ratio. $\frac{35}{110} = \frac{7}{22}$
4. Write each ratio. Then write an equal ratio that has the same number of total beads as the ratio in Item 3.

   a. white beads:total beads $\frac{30}{110}, \frac{6}{22}$ b. red beads:total beads $\frac{45}{110}, \frac{9}{22}$

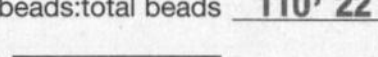

Solve

5. In the smaller bracelet, how many beads are

   a. there in all? **22 beads.** b. white? **6 beads.**

   c. red? **9 beads.** d. blue? **7 beads.**

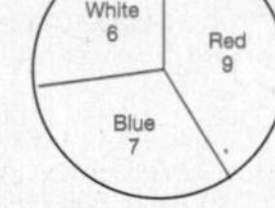

6. Use your answers to Item 5 to draw a circle graph.

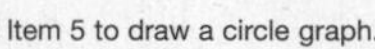

Look Back

7. Did the size of each section in your circle graph change from the size in the graph at the top of the page? Explain. **No, because the proportion of each color to the total did not change.**

SOLVE ANOTHER PROBLEM

Carole wants to make a larger bracelet using the same ratios of colors as in the circle graph at the top of the page. Draw a circle graph that shows how many beads of each color Carole could use.

Possible answer:

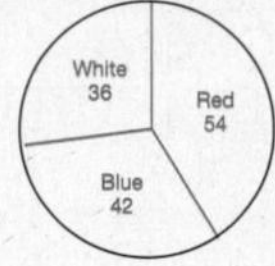

Name ______________________

Guided Problem Solving 10-3

GPS PROBLEM 21, PAGE 526

Cameron is making decorations for "Back to School Night." He can make 2 posters in an hour. At this rate, how long will it take him to make 5 posters? Explain.

Understand

1. Circle how many posters Cameron can make in one hour.
2. Underline what you are asked to find.

Plan

3. What is the unit rate to make the posters? **2 posters:1 hour.**
4. How many minutes in one hour? **60 minutes.**
5. Write the rate as posters to minutes. **2 posters: 60 minutes.**
6. Complete the table to find an equal rate.

Posters	1	**2**	3	**4**	5
Minutes	**30**	60	**90**	120	**150**

Solve

7. How long will it take Cameron to make 5 posters? **150 minutes.**
8. How many *hours* will it take Cameron to make 5 posters? **$2\frac{1}{2}$ hours.**
9. Explain how you found your answer. **Possible answer: Convert hours to minutes, then find equal rates.**

Look Back

10. What is another way to find how long it would take Cameron to make 5 posters? **Possible answer: Multiply the unit rate $\frac{2 \text{ posters}}{1 \text{ hour}}$ by $\frac{2.5}{2.5}$.**

SOLVE ANOTHER PROBLEM

Morgan can make 48 cookies in an hour. At this rate, how long will it take her to make 60 cookies? **$1\frac{1}{4}$ hours.**

Name ______________________

Guided Problem Solving 10-4

GPS PROBLEM 25, PAGE 533

Janice can run 100 meters in 12 seconds. Carl can run 500 meters in 48 seconds. Susan runs at a rate of 10 meters per second. Phillip can run 200 meters in 24 seconds. Which two students run at the same rate? Explain how you found your answer.

Understand

Possible answer: Item 6

1. Underline the question.
2. Write the rate that each student runs in meters per seconds.

   a. Janice $\frac{100}{12}$ b. Carl $\frac{500}{48}$ c. Susan $\frac{10}{1}$ d. Phillip $\frac{200}{24}$

Plan

3. Make an organized list to compare the pairs of rates.

   a. Janice and Carl $\frac{100}{12} \stackrel{?}{=} \frac{500}{48}$ b. Janice and Susan $\frac{100}{12} \stackrel{?}{=} \frac{10}{1}$

   c. Janice and Phillip $\frac{100}{12} \stackrel{?}{=} \frac{200}{24}$ d. Carl and Susan $\frac{500}{48} \stackrel{?}{=} \frac{10}{1}$

   e. Carl and Phillip $\frac{500}{48} \stackrel{?}{=} \frac{200}{24}$ f. Susan and Phillip $\frac{10}{1} \stackrel{?}{=} \frac{200}{24}$

Solve

4. Which of the pairs of rates in Item 3 form a proportion? $\frac{100}{12} = \frac{200}{24}$
5. Which students run at the same rate? Explain. **Possible answer: Janice and Phillip, since they have equal rates.**

Look Back

6. How could you find which students run at the same rate by writing each rate in lowest terms. **Equal rates will be the same when written in lowest terms.**

SOLVE ANOTHER PROBLEM

Guillermo made $15 for baby-sitting 5 hours. Megan made $28 in 8 hours. Thomas earned $2.50 in 1 hour, and Della earned $14 in 4 hours. Which two students were paid the same rate? Explain. **Megan and Della; They were each paid $3.50 per hour.**

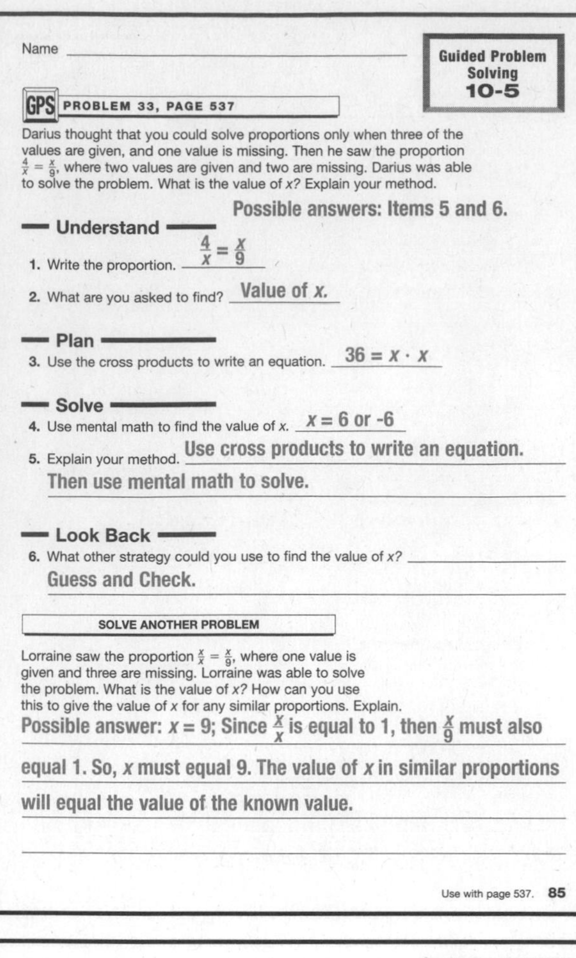

Name ______________________

Guided Problem Solving 10-5

GPS PROBLEM 33, PAGE 537

Darius thought that you could solve proportions only when three of the values are given, and one value is missing. Then he saw the proportion $\frac{4}{x} = \frac{x}{9}$, where two values are given and two are missing. Darius was able to solve the problem. What is the value of x? Explain your method.

Possible answers: Items 5 and 6.

— Understand —

1. Write the proportion. $\frac{4}{x} = \frac{x}{9}$
2. What are you asked to find? Value of x.

— Plan —

3. Use the cross products to write an equation. $36 = x \cdot x$

— Solve —

4. Use mental math to find the value of x. $x = 6$ or -6
5. Explain your method. Use cross products to write an equation. Then use mental math to solve.

— Look Back —

6. What other strategy could you use to find the value of x? Guess and Check.

SOLVE ANOTHER PROBLEM

Lorraine saw the proportion $\frac{x}{x} = \frac{x}{9}$, where one value is given and three are missing. Lorraine was able to solve the problem. What is the value of x? How can you use this to give the value of x for any similar proportions. Explain.

Possible answer: $x = 9$; Since $\frac{x}{x}$ is equal to 1, then $\frac{x}{9}$ must also equal 1. So, x must equal 9. The value of x in similar proportions will equal the value of the known value.

Use with page 537. 85

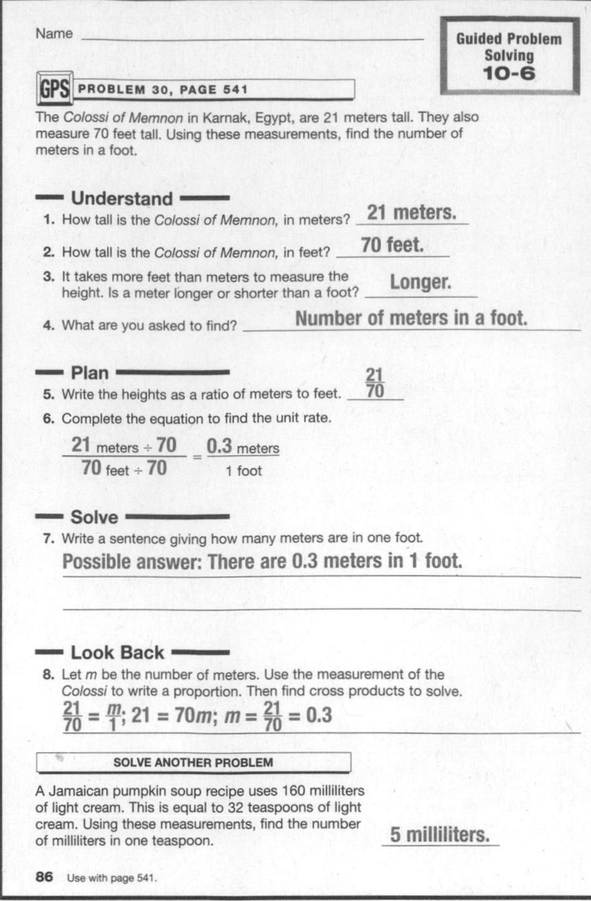

Name ______________________

Guided Problem Solving 10-6

GPS PROBLEM 30, PAGE 541

The *Colossi of Memnon* in Karnak, Egypt, are 21 meters tall. They also measure 70 feet tall. Using these measurements, find the number of meters in a foot.

— Understand —

1. How tall is the *Colossi of Memnon*, in meters? 21 meters.
2. How tall is the *Colossi of Memnon*, in feet? 70 feet.
3. It takes more feet than meters to measure the height. Is a meter longer or shorter than a foot? Longer.
4. What are you asked to find? Number of meters in a foot.

— Plan —

5. Write the heights as a ratio of meters to feet. $\frac{21}{70}$
6. Complete the equation to find the unit rate.

$$\frac{21 \text{ meters} \div 70}{70 \text{ feet} \div 70} = \frac{0.3 \text{ meters}}{1 \text{ foot}}$$

— Solve —

7. Write a sentence giving how many meters are in one foot. Possible answer: There are 0.3 meters in 1 foot.

— Look Back —

8. Let m be the number of meters. Use the measurement of the *Colossi* to write a proportion. Then find cross products to solve. $\frac{21}{70} = \frac{m}{1}$; $21 = 70m$; $m = \frac{21}{70} = 0.3$

SOLVE ANOTHER PROBLEM

A Jamaican pumpkin soup recipe uses 160 milliliters of light cream. This is equal to 32 teaspoons of light cream. Using these measurements, find the number of milliliters in one teaspoon. 5 milliliters.

86 Use with page 541.

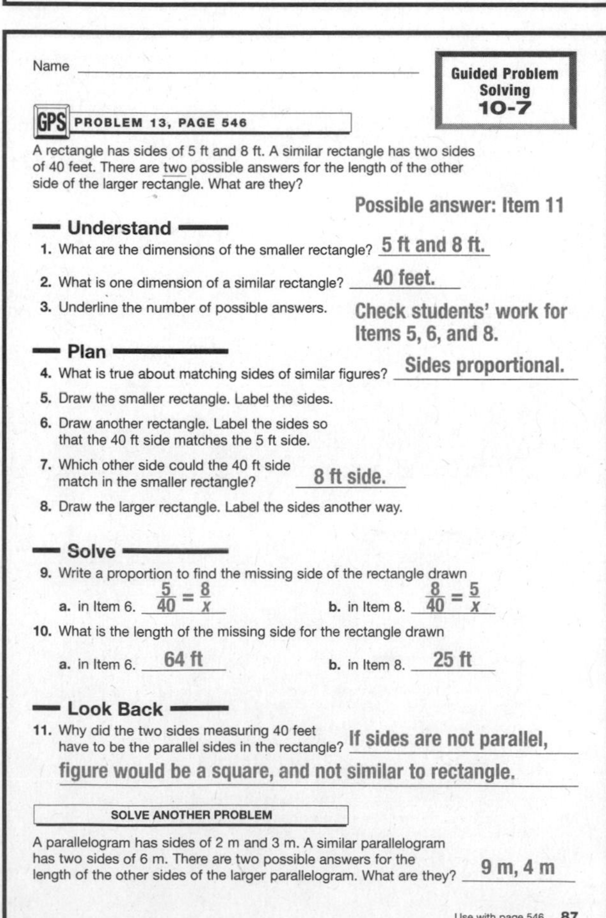

Name ______________________

Guided Problem Solving 10-7

GPS PROBLEM 13, PAGE 546

A rectangle has sides of 5 ft and 8 ft. A similar rectangle has two sides of 40 feet. There are two possible answers for the length of the other side of the larger rectangle. What are they?

Possible answer: Item 11

— Understand —

1. What are the dimensions of the smaller rectangle? 5 ft and 8 ft.
2. What is one dimension of a similar rectangle? 40 feet.
3. Underline the number of possible answers. Check students' work for Items 5, 6, and 8.

— Plan —

4. What is true about matching sides of similar figures? Sides proportional.
5. Draw the smaller rectangle. Label the sides.
6. Draw another rectangle. Label the sides so that the 40 ft side matches the 5 ft side.
7. Which other side could the 40 ft side match in the smaller rectangle? 8 ft side.
8. Draw the larger rectangle. Label the sides another way.

— Solve —

9. Write a proportion to find the missing side of the rectangle drawn
   a. in Item 6. $\frac{5}{40} = \frac{8}{x}$ b. in Item 8. $\frac{8}{40} = \frac{5}{x}$
10. What is the length of the missing side for the rectangle drawn
    a. in Item 6. 64 ft b. in Item 8. 25 ft

— Look Back —

11. Why did the two sides measuring 40 feet have to be the parallel sides in the rectangle? If sides are not parallel, figure would be a square, and not similar to rectangle.

SOLVE ANOTHER PROBLEM

A parallelogram has sides of 2 m and 3 m. A similar parallelogram has two sides of 6 m. There are two possible answers for the length of the other sides of the larger parallelogram. What are they? 9 m, 4 m

Use with page 546. 87

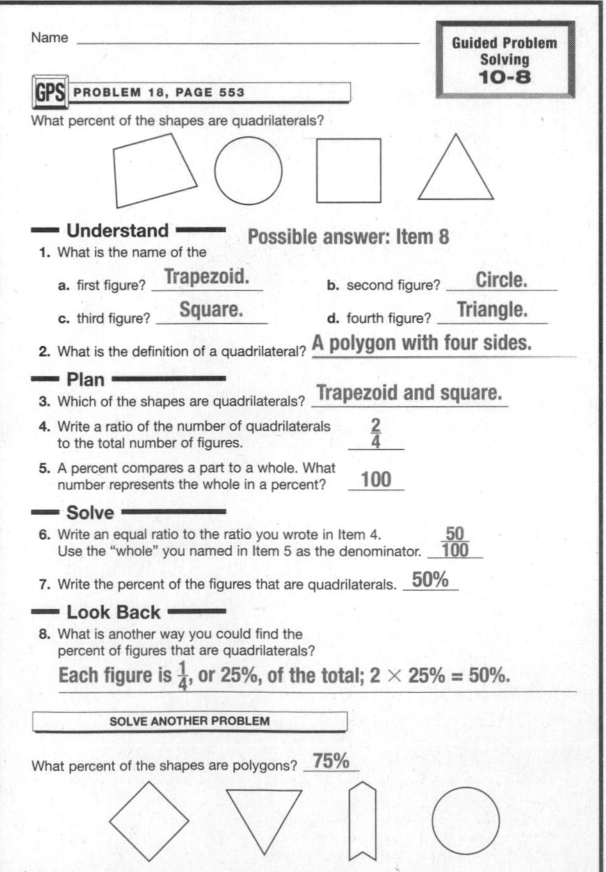

Name ______________________

Guided Problem Solving 10-8

GPS PROBLEM 18, PAGE 553

What percent of the shapes are quadrilaterals?

— Understand —

Possible answer: Item 8

1. What is the name of the
   a. first figure? Trapezoid. b. second figure? Circle.
   c. third figure? Square. d. fourth figure? Triangle.
2. What is the definition of a quadrilateral? A polygon with four sides.

— Plan —

3. Which of the shapes are quadrilaterals? Trapezoid and square.
4. Write a ratio of the number of quadrilaterals to the total number of figures. $\frac{2}{4}$
5. A percent compares a part to a whole. What number represents the whole in a percent? 100

— Solve —

6. Write an equal ratio to the ratio you wrote in Item 4. Use the "whole" you named in Item 5 as the denominator. $\frac{50}{100}$
7. Write the percent of the figures that are quadrilaterals. 50%

— Look Back —

8. What is another way you could find the percent of figures that are quadrilaterals? Each figure is $\frac{1}{4}$, or 25%, of the total; $2 \times 25\% = 50\%$.

SOLVE ANOTHER PROBLEM

What percent of the shapes are polygons? 75%

88 Use with page 553.

Name ______________________

Guided Problem Solving 10-9

GPS **PROBLEM 30, PAGE 557**

If a shirt was originally $20, went on sale for 15% off, and then was put on clearance with an additional 45% off, estimate the clearance price of the shirt. Explain your reasoning.

Possible answers: Items 9 and 10

Understand

1. What was the original price of the shirt? $20
2. What was the first discount? 15% The second discount? 45%

Plan

3. Is 15% closer to $\frac{1}{10}$, $\frac{2}{10}$, or $\frac{1}{4}$? $\frac{2}{10}$
4. Is 45% closer to $\frac{1}{4}$, $\frac{4}{10}$, or $\frac{1}{2}$? $\frac{1}{2}$

Solve

5. Use the fraction in Item 3 to estimate 15% of $20. $4
6. Subtract the discount to find the first clearance price. $16
7. Use the fraction in Item 4 to estimate 45% of the first clearance price. $8
8. Subtract the discount to find the second clearance price. $8
9. Explain your reasoning. Estimated the first clearance price, then used that price to estimate the second clearance price.

Look Back

10. Do you think your estimated clearance price is higher or lower than the actual clearance price. Explain. Lower than; Estimated fractions are greater than actual percents.

SOLVE ANOTHER PROBLEM

If a jacket was originally $90, went on sale for 30% off, and then was put on clearance with an additional 15% off, estimate the clearance price of the jacket. Explain your reasoning. Possible answer: $48

30% of 90 ≈ $30; 15% of $60 ≈ $12; $60 – $12 = $48

Name ______________________

Guided Problem Solving 10-10

GPS **PROBLEM 57, PAGE 562**

45% of the students at Suburban High School are boys. 30% of the boys at Suburban High School have curly hair. What fraction of the students at Suburban High School are boys with curly hair?

Understand

1. What percent of the students at Suburban High are boys? 45%
2. What percent of the boys at Suburban High have curly hair? 30%
3. Are you going to write your answer as a percent, a decimal, or a fraction? A fraction.

Plan

4. Suppose you were given the number of boys at Suburban High. How would you find how many boys have curly hair? Multiply the number of boys by the fraction of boys with curly hair.
5. You know the fraction of boys in the school rather than the number of boys. Which operation will you use to find what fraction of students are boys with curly hair? Multiplication.
6. Write the number of students that are boys as a fraction. Then rewrite the fraction in lowest terms. $\frac{45}{100}$, $\frac{9}{20}$
7. Write the number of boys that have curly hair as a fraction. Then rewrite the fraction in lowest terms. $\frac{30}{100}$, $\frac{3}{10}$

Solve

8. Write an expression to find the fraction of students that are boys with curly hair. $\frac{9}{20} \times \frac{3}{10}$
9. What fraction of the students at Suburban High are boys with curly hair? $\frac{27}{200}$

Look Back

10. Show how to estimate to see if your answer is reasonable. 45% is about $\frac{1}{2}$; 30% is about $\frac{1}{4}$; $\frac{1}{2} \times \frac{1}{4} = \frac{1}{8}$; $\frac{1}{8} = \frac{25}{200}$ which is about $\frac{27}{200}$.

SOLVE ANOTHER PROBLEM

20% of the houses on the block are white. 65% of the white houses have blue trim. What fraction of these houses are white with blue trim? $\frac{13}{100}$

Name ______________________

Guided Problem Solving 10-11

GPS **PROBLEM 42, PAGE 567**

A new student's score on a spelling test was about 72% of Catherine's score. Catherine's score was about 98% of Tom's score. Tom's score was about 94% of Luanna's score. Luanna got 93 out of 100 points. How many points did the new student get?

Possible answer: Item 4

Understand

1. How many points did Luanna score on the spelling test? 93 points.
2. Underline how each student's score relates to another student's score such as, 72% of Catherine's.

Plan

3. Which strategy will you use to find the new student's score? c
   a. Look for a Pattern b. Draw a Diagram c. Work Backward
4. What operation do you use to find a percent of a number? Multiplication.
5. There are no fractional points given for partially correct answers. What should you do if your answer is a decimal? Round to the nearest whole number.

Solve

6. How many points did Tom score? 87 points.
7. How many points did Catherine score? 85 points.
8. How many points did the new student score? 61 points.

Look Back

9. Order the students scores from least to greatest. Does this correspond with the clues given in the problem? New student, Catherine, Tom, Luanna; Yes.

SOLVE ANOTHER PROBLEM

Eden's bowling score was about 96% of Remy's score. Remy's score was about 75% of Laneesha's score. Laneesha's score was 100% of Martin's score. Martin's bowling score was 150 points. How many points did the Eden score? 108 points.

Name ______________________

Guided Problem Solving 11-1

GPS **PROBLEM 23, STUDENT PAGE 583**

Use what you know about triangular, rectangular, and pentagonal prisms to draw a hexagonal prism. Classify each of the faces and explain your drawing.

Understand

1. What are you asked to draw? Hexagonal prism.
2. Does a prism have one base or two parallel, congruent bases? Two bases.

Plan

3. What polygon makes up the base for each of these prisms?
   a. Triangular Triangle. b. Rectangular Rectangle.
   c. Pentagonal Pentagon.
4. What polygon will make up the base of a hexagonal prism? Hexagon.
5. What polygon makes up the sides for each of the three given prisms? Rectangle.
6. What polygon will make up the sides of a hexagonal prism? Rectangle.

Solve

7. Draw a hexagonal prism. Possible answer:
8. Explain your drawing. 3-D shape; 2 hexagonal bases; 6 rectangular sides.

Look Back

9. What is the pattern in the number of faces in triangular, rectangular, and pentagonal prisms? How many faces will be in a hexagonal prism? Possible answer: The pattern of faces increases by 1: 5, 6, 7... so there will be 8 faces in the hexagon.

SOLVE ANOTHER PROBLEM

Draw an octagonal prism. Classify each of the faces and explain your drawing? Possible answer:

3-D shape; 2 octagonal bases; 8 rectangular sides.

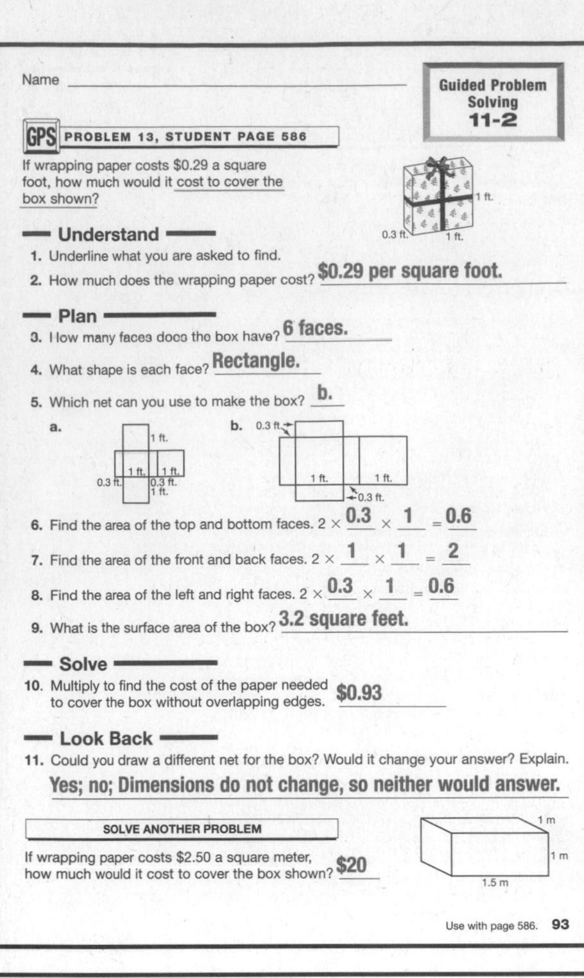

Name ______________________

Guided Problem Solving 11-2

GPS PROBLEM 13, STUDENT PAGE 586

If wrapping paper costs $0.29 a square foot, how much would it cost to cover the box shown?

Understand

1. Underline what you are asked to find.
2. How much does the wrapping paper cost? **$0.29 per square foot.**

Plan

3. How many faces does the box have? **6 faces.**
4. What shape is each face? **Rectangle.**
5. Which net can you use to make the box? **b.**

a. b.

6. Find the area of the top and bottom faces. 2 × **0.3** × **1** = **0.6**
7. Find the area of the front and back faces. 2 × **1** × **1** = **2**
8. Find the area of the left and right faces. 2 × **0.3** × **1** = **0.6**
9. What is the surface area of the box? **3.2 square feet.**

Solve

10. Multiply to find the cost of the paper needed to cover the box without overlapping edges. **$0.93**

Look Back

11. Could you draw a different net for the box? Would it change your answer? Explain.
Yes; no; Dimensions do not change, so neither would answer.

SOLVE ANOTHER PROBLEM

If wrapping paper costs $2.50 a square meter, how much would it cost to cover the box shown? **$20**

Use with page 586. 93

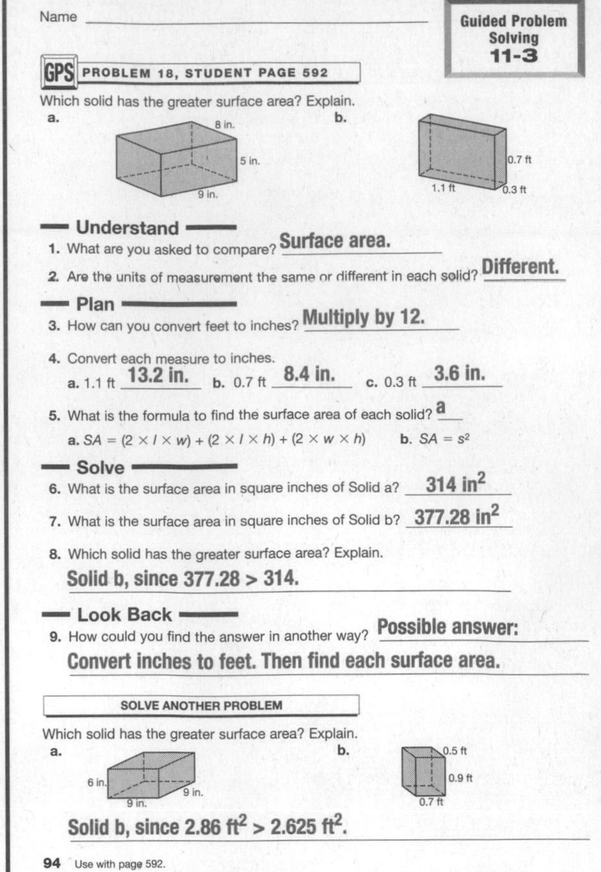

Name ______________________

Guided Problem Solving 11-3

GPS PROBLEM 18, STUDENT PAGE 592

Which solid has the greater surface area? Explain.

a. b.

Understand

1. What are you asked to compare? **Surface area.**
2. Are the units of measurement the same or different in each solid? **Different.**

Plan

3. How can you convert feet to inches? **Multiply by 12.**
4. Convert each measure to inches.
a. 1.1 ft **13.2 in.** b. 0.7 ft **8.4 in.** c. 0.3 ft **3.6 in.**
5. What is the formula to find the surface area of each solid? **a**
a. $SA = (2 \times l \times w) + (2 \times l \times h) + (2 \times w \times h)$ b. $SA = s^2$

Solve

6. What is the surface area in square inches of Solid a? **314 in^2**
7. What is the surface area in square inches of Solid b? **377.28 in^2**
8. Which solid has the greater surface area? Explain.
Solid b, since 377.28 > 314.

Look Back

9. How could you find the answer in another way? **Possible answer:**
Convert inches to feet. Then find each surface area.

SOLVE ANOTHER PROBLEM

Which solid has the greater surface area? Explain.

a. b.

Solid b, since 2.86 ft^2 > 2.625 ft^2.

94 Use with page 592.

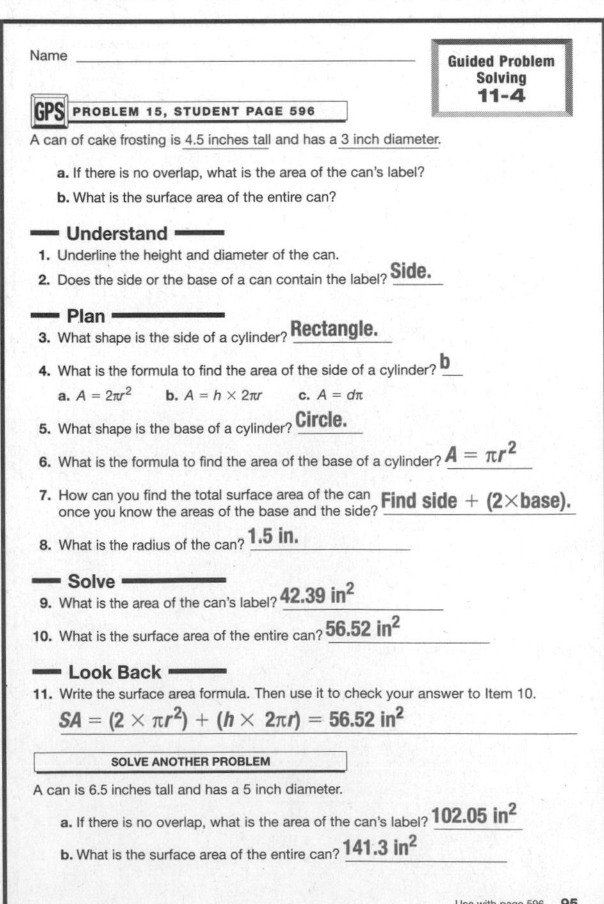

Name ______________________

Guided Problem Solving 11-4

GPS PROBLEM 15, STUDENT PAGE 596

A can of cake frosting is 4.5 inches tall and has a 3 inch diameter.

a. If there is no overlap, what is the area of the can's label?
b. What is the surface area of the entire can?

Understand

1. Underline the height and diameter of the can.
2. Does the side or the base of a can contain the label? **Side.**

Plan

3. What shape is the side of a cylinder? **Rectangle.**
4. What is the formula to find the area of the side of a cylinder? **b**
a. $A = 2\pi r^2$ b. $A = h \times 2\pi r$ c. $A = d\pi$
5. What shape is the base of a cylinder? **Circle.**
6. What is the formula to find the area of the base of a cylinder? $A = \pi r^2$
7. How can you find the total surface area of the can once you know the areas of the base and the side? **Find side + (2×base).**
8. What is the radius of the can? **1.5 in.**

Solve

9. What is the area of the can's label? **42.39 in^2**
10. What is the surface area of the entire can? **56.52 in^2**

Look Back

11. Write the surface area formula. Then use it to check your answer to Item 10.
$SA = (2 \times \pi r^2) + (h \times 2\pi r) = 56.52 \text{ in}^2$

SOLVE ANOTHER PROBLEM

A can is 6.5 inches tall and has a 5 inch diameter.

a. If there is no overlap, what is the area of the can's label? **102.05 in^2**
b. What is the surface area of the entire can? **141.3 in^2**

Use with page 596. 95

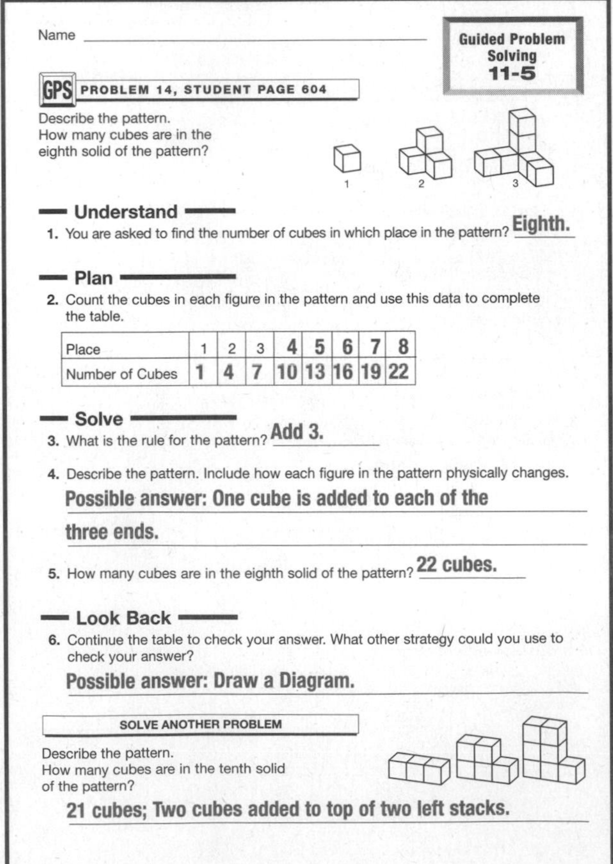

Name ______________________

Guided Problem Solving 11-5

GPS PROBLEM 14, STUDENT PAGE 604

Describe the pattern.
How many cubes are in the eighth solid of the pattern?

Understand

1. You are asked to find the number of cubes in which place in the pattern? **Eighth.**

Plan

2. Count the cubes in each figure in the pattern and use this data to complete the table.

Place	1	2	3	4	5	6	7	8
Number of Cubes	1	4	7	10	13	16	19	22

Solve

3. What is the rule for the pattern? **Add 3.**
4. Describe the pattern. Include how each figure in the pattern physically changes.
Possible answer: One cube is added to each of the three ends.
5. How many cubes are in the eighth solid of the pattern? **22 cubes.**

Look Back

6. Continue the table to check your answer. What other strategy could you use to check your answer?
Possible answer: Draw a Diagram.

SOLVE ANOTHER PROBLEM

Describe the pattern.
How many cubes are in the tenth solid of the pattern?

21 cubes; Two cubes added to top of two left stacks.

96 Use with page 604.

Name ______________________

Guided Problem Solving 11-6

GPS PROBLEM 11, STUDENT PAGE 608

When sugar cubes are produced, they are put into tightly packed boxes for purchasing. If the box of sugar cubes shown is 3 cubes high, how many sugar cubes are in the box?

Understand

1. How many sugar cubes high is the box? **3 cubes.**
2. What are you asked to find? **Number of cubes in box.**

Plan

3. How many cubes are in one row? **6 cubes.**
4. How many cubes are in one column? **7 cubes.**
5. How many cubes are in one layer? **42 cubes.**

Solve

6. Complete the number sentence to find the number of sugar cubes in the box. **3** × **42** = **126**
7. Write a sentence giving the number of cubes in the box. **Possible answer: There are 126 sugar cubes in the box.**

Look Back

8. Draw a diagram of each layer of sugar cubes. Make sure that the number of cubes matches your answer to Item 6. **Possible answer:**

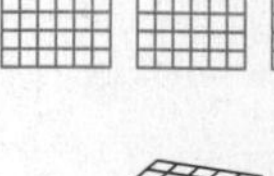

SOLVE ANOTHER PROBLEM

Centimeter cubes can be placed in tightly packed boxes. If the box of centimeter cubes shown is 4 cubes high, how many centimeter cubes are in the box?

100 cubes.

Name ______________________

Guided Problem Solving 11-7

GPS PROBLEM 17, STUDENT PAGE 614

The volume of a gallon of water is about 231 cubic inches. If a 25-gallon aquarium is 32 inches long and 15 inches wide, how deep is it? Explain.

Understand

1. What are you asked to find? **Depth (height) of an aquarium.**
2. What is the volume of a gallon of water? **231 cubic inches.**
3. Underline the dimensions of the aquarium that are given.

Plan

4. How can you find the volume of an aquarium that holds 25 gallons of water? **Multiply 25 and 231.**
5. What is the volume of the aquarium? **5775 cubic inches.**
6. What is the formula to find the volume of a rectangular prism? $V = l \times w \times h$
7. Substitute known values into the equation you wrote in Item 6. $5775 = 32 \times 15 \times h$

Solve

8. Multiply values in the equation. $5775 = 480 \times h$
9. Use mental math, or guess and check to find the depth of the aquarium to the nearest whole number. $h \approx 12$
10. How deep is the aquarium? Explain. **About 12 inches;** $12 \times 32 \times 15 \approx 25 \times 231$.

Look Back

11. Estimate to see if your answer is reasonable. **Possible answer: Since** $10 \times 30 \times 20 = 30 \times 200$**, the answer is reasonable.**

SOLVE ANOTHER PROBLEM

The volume of a gallon of water is about 231 cubic inches. If a 30-gallon aquarium is 25 inches long and 25 inches wide, how deep is it? Explain.

About 11 in.; $25 \times 25 \times 11 \approx 30 \times 231$

Name ______________________

Guided Problem Solving 12-1

GPS PROBLEM 14, STUDENT PAGE 628

Suppose you roll a number cube. Find *P*(even number).

Understand

1. What does the problem ask you to find? **The probability of rolling an even number.**

Plan

2. How many numbers are on a number cube? **6 numbers.**
3. How many possible outcomes are there when you roll a number cube? **6**
4. What are the even numbers on a number cube? **2, 4, and 6**
5. How many ways can you roll an even number? **3 ways.**

Solve

6. Write the probability of rolling an even number. Which ratio will you use? **a**

   a. $P(\text{event}) = \frac{\text{number of ways event can happen}}{\text{number of possible outcomes}}$

   b. $P(\text{event}) = \frac{\text{number of possible outcomes}}{\text{number of ways event can happen}}$

7. Write the probability. $P(\text{even number}) = \frac{3}{6}$ or $\frac{1}{2}$

Look Back

7. Are all the possible outcomes equally likely? How do you know? **Yes. Each has an equal chance of occurring.**

SOLVE ANOTHER PROBLEM

Suppose you toss a twelve-sided number cube with numbers 1-12 on its faces. What is the probability of rolling a number which is a multiple of 5?

$\frac{2}{12}$ or $\frac{1}{6}$

Name ______________________

Guided Problem Solving 12-2

GPS PROBLEM 15, STUDENT PAGE 633

Hurricane season in the United States is from June 1 to November 30. In an average season, there are ten tropical storms. Six are expected to reach hurricane strength and two of these are likely to strike the U.S. coast.

Is the probability that a tropical storm will turn into a hurricane more than 50%?

Understand

1. How many tropical storms are there in an average season? **10 storms.**
2. How many of the tropical storms are expected to reach hurricane strength in an average season? **6 storms.**

Plan

3. Describe the ratio you will use to show the probability that a tropical storm will turn into a hurricane. **Number of tropical storms expected to reach hurricane strength: Number of tropical storms.**
4. What will you compare the ratio to? **The probability of 50%.**

Solve

5. Find the probability that a tropical storm will turn into a hurricane. $\frac{6}{10}$ or $\frac{3}{5}$
6. Write the probability as a percent. **60%**
7. Is the percentage less than, equal to, or greater than 50%? **Greater than.**

Look Back

8. How could you answer the question without changing the probability to a percent? **50% is equal to** $\frac{1}{2}$**. The probability is** $\frac{3}{5}$**. Since** $\frac{3}{5} > \frac{1}{2}$**, the probability of** $\frac{3}{5}$ **is greater than 50%.**

SOLVE ANOTHER PROBLEM

Suppose 20 tropical storms are predicted. Twelve are expected to reach hurricane strength. What percentage will probably *not* become hurricanes? **40%**

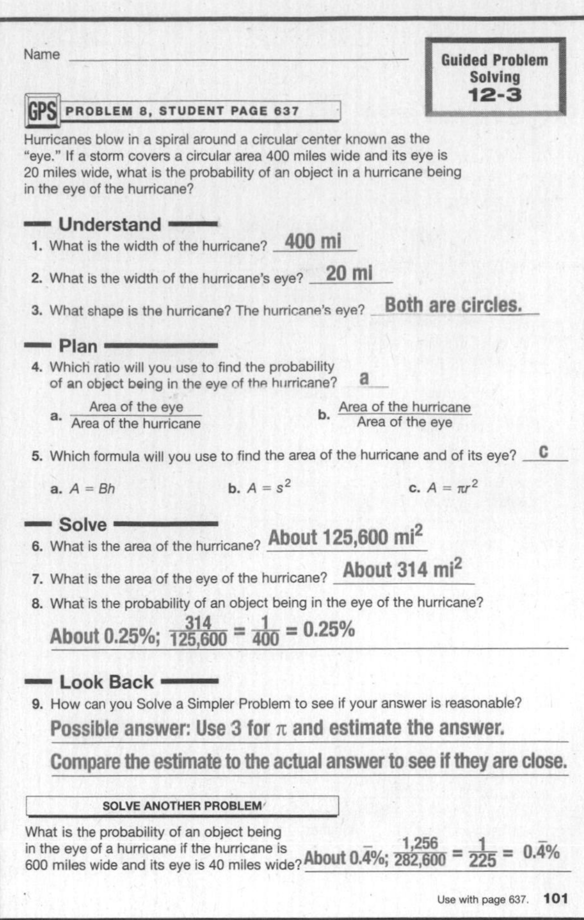

Name ______________________

Guided Problem Solving 12-3

GPS PROBLEM 8, STUDENT PAGE 637

Hurricanes blow in a spiral around a circular center known as the "eye." If a storm covers a circular area 400 miles wide and its eye is 20 miles wide, what is the probability of an object in a hurricane being in the eye of the hurricane?

Understand

1. What is the width of the hurricane? **400 mi**
2. What is the width of the hurricane's eye? **20 mi**
3. What shape is the hurricane? The hurricane's eye? **Both are circles.**

Plan

4. Which ratio will you use to find the probability of an object being in the eye of the hurricane? **a**

   a. $\frac{\text{Area of the eye}}{\text{Area of the hurricane}}$ b. $\frac{\text{Area of the hurricane}}{\text{Area of the eye}}$

5. Which formula will you use to find the area of the hurricane and of its eye? **c**

   a. $A = Bh$ b. $A = s^2$ c. $A = \pi r^2$

Solve

6. What is the area of the hurricane? **About 125,600 mi^2**
7. What is the area of the eye of the hurricane? **About 314 mi^2**
8. What is the probability of an object being in the eye of the hurricane?

   About 0.25%; $\frac{314}{125{,}600} = \frac{1}{400} = 0.25\%$

Look Back

9. How can you Solve a Simpler Problem to see if your answer is reasonable?

   Possible answer: Use 3 for π and estimate the answer. Compare the estimate to the actual answer to see if they are close.

SOLVE ANOTHER PROBLEM

What is the probability of an object being in the eye of a hurricane if the hurricane is 600 miles wide and its eye is 40 miles wide? **About $0.\overline{4}\%$; $\frac{1{,}256}{282{,}600} = \frac{1}{225} = 0.\overline{4}\%$**

Use with page 637. 101

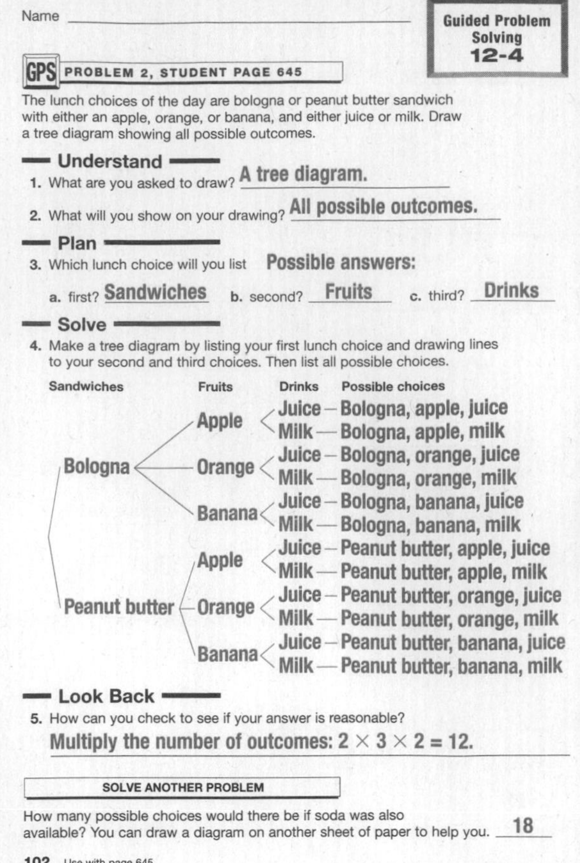

Name ______________________

Guided Problem Solving 12-4

GPS PROBLEM 2, STUDENT PAGE 645

The lunch choices of the day are bologna or peanut butter sandwich with either an apple, orange, or banana, and either juice or milk. Draw a tree diagram showing all possible outcomes.

Understand

1. What are you asked to draw? **A tree diagram.**
2. What will you show on your drawing? **All possible outcomes.**

Plan

3. Which lunch choice will you list **Possible answers:**

   a. first? **Sandwiches** b. second? **Fruits** c. third? **Drinks**

Solve

4. Make a tree diagram by listing your first lunch choice and drawing lines to your second and third choices. Then list all possible choices.

Sandwiches	Fruits	Drinks	Possible choices
Bologna	**Apple**	**Juice**	**Bologna, apple, juice**
		Milk	**Bologna, apple, milk**
	Orange	**Juice**	**Bologna, orange, juice**
		Milk	**Bologna, orange, milk**
	Banana	**Juice**	**Bologna, banana, juice**
		Milk	**Bologna, banana, milk**
Peanut butter	**Apple**	**Juice**	**Peanut butter, apple, juice**
		Milk	**Peanut butter, apple, milk**
	Orange	**Juice**	**Peanut butter, orange, juice**
		Milk	**Peanut butter, orange, milk**
	Banana	**Juice**	**Peanut butter, banana, juice**
		Milk	**Peanut butter, banana, milk**

Look Back

5. How can you check to see if your answer is reasonable?

   Multiply the number of outcomes: $2 \times 3 \times 2 = 12$.

SOLVE ANOTHER PROBLEM

How many possible choices would there be if soda was also available? You can draw a diagram on another sheet of paper to help you. **18**

102 Use with page 645.

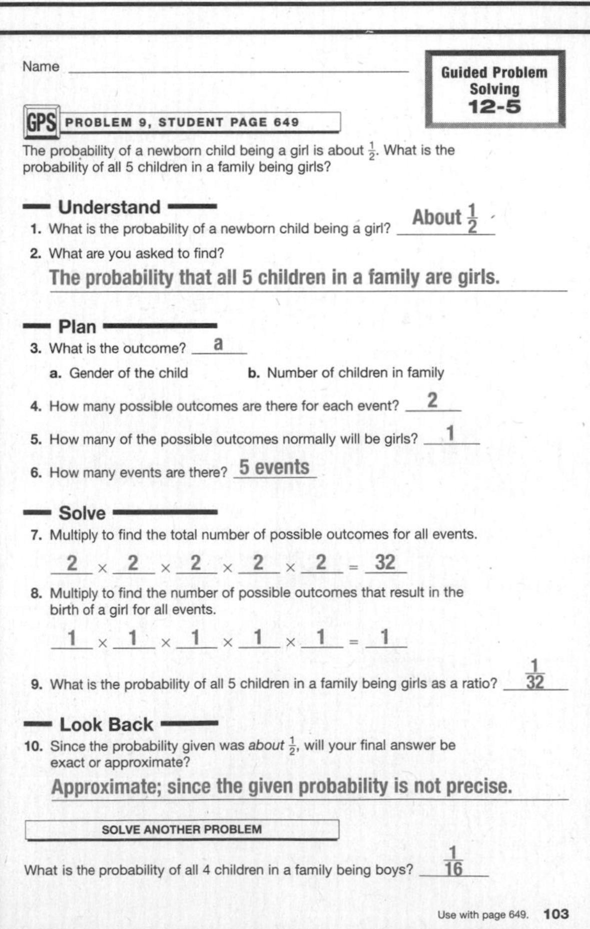

Name ______________________

Guided Problem Solving 12-5

GPS PROBLEM 9, STUDENT PAGE 649

The probability of a newborn child being a girl is about $\frac{1}{2}$. What is the probability of all 5 children in a family being girls?

Understand

1. What is the probability of a newborn child being a girl? **About $\frac{1}{2}$**
2. What are you asked to find?

   The probability that all 5 children in a family are girls.

Plan

3. What is the outcome? **a**

   a. Gender of the child b. Number of children in family

4. How many possible outcomes are there for each event? **2**
5. How many of the possible outcomes normally will be girls? **1**
6. How many events are there? **5 events**

Solve

7. Multiply to find the total number of possible outcomes for all events.

   2 × **2** × **2** × **2** × **2** = **32**

8. Multiply to find the number of possible outcomes that result in the birth of a girl for all events.

   1 × **1** × **1** × **1** × **1** = **1**

9. What is the probability of all 5 children in a family being girls as a ratio? **$\frac{1}{32}$**

Look Back

10. Since the probability given was *about* $\frac{1}{2}$, will your final answer be exact or approximate?

    Approximate; since the given probability is not precise.

SOLVE ANOTHER PROBLEM

What is the probability of all 4 children in a family being boys? **$\frac{1}{16}$**

Use with page 649. 103

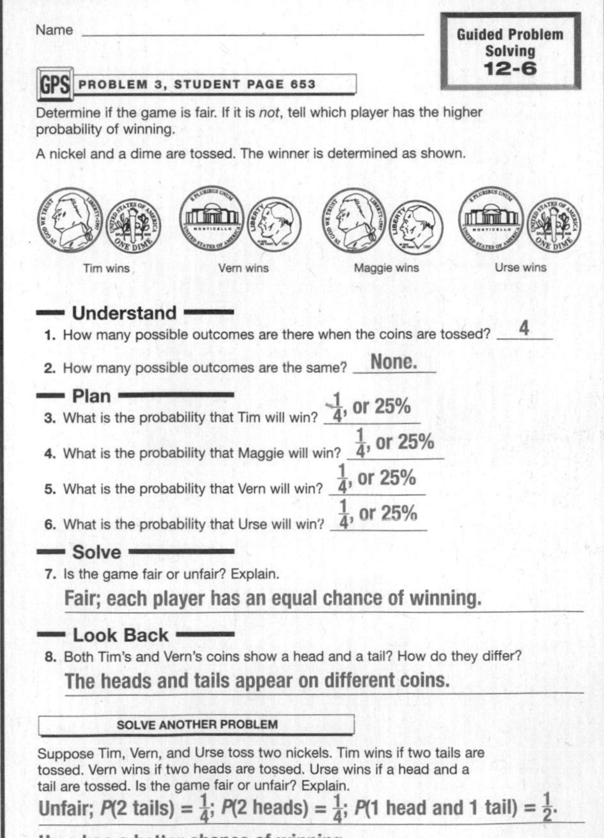

Name ______________________

Guided Problem Solving 12-6

GPS PROBLEM 3, STUDENT PAGE 653

Determine if the game is fair. If it is *not*, tell which player has the higher probability of winning.

A nickel and a dime are tossed. The winner is determined as shown.

Understand

1. How many possible outcomes are there when the coins are tossed? **4**
2. How many possible outcomes are the same? **None.**

Plan

3. What is the probability that Tim will win? **$\frac{1}{4}$, or 25%**
4. What is the probability that Maggie will win? **$\frac{1}{4}$, or 25%**
5. What is the probability that Vern will win? **$\frac{1}{4}$, or 25%**
6. What is the probability that Urse will win? **$\frac{1}{4}$, or 25%**

Solve

7. Is the game fair or unfair? Explain.

   Fair; each player has an equal chance of winning.

Look Back

8. Both Tim's and Vern's coins show a head and a tail? How do they differ?

   The heads and tails appear on different coins.

SOLVE ANOTHER PROBLEM

Suppose Tim, Vern, and Urse toss two nickels. Tim wins if two tails are tossed. Vern wins if two heads are tossed. Urse wins if a head and a tail are tossed. Is the game fair or unfair? Explain.

Unfair; P(2 tails) = $\frac{1}{4}$; P(2 heads) = $\frac{1}{4}$; P(1 head and 1 tail) = $\frac{1}{2}$. Urse has a better chance of winning.

104 Use with page 653.